EZEKIEL'S MIRACLE

THE DISCOVERY OF INSULIN

BY
G. BARCLAY ROBERTSON

Published by

MELROSE BOOKS

An Imprint of Melrose Press Limited
St Thomas Place, Ely
Cambridgeshire
CB7 4GG, UK
www.melrosebooks.co.uk

FIRST EDITION

Cover designed by Catherine McIntyre
Cover picture: James Collip in lab. circa 1914

ISBN 978-1-908645-05-0

Printed and bound in Great Britain by:
Mimeo Ltd, Huntingdon, Cambridgeshire

ABOUT THE AUTHOR

G. Barclay Robertson, best known as 'Barry', wrote this book because, now eighty, he was diagnosed as an Insulin Dependent diabetic (Type 1) in 1948, the year the NHS arrived. Educated at Leith Academy in Edinburgh, with English as his best subject, his ambition was to become a journalist, but the 'men in the white coats' at Edinburgh Royal Infirmary rejected his choice.

'You'll need daily injections (now four), a strict diet taken at set times… 'No, no, think of something else.'

His uncles owned a big wholesale ironmongery business in Dundee, so the 'something else' finished up with a three-year apprenticeship with a well-known engineer, mill furnisher and machine tool merchant in Edinburgh.

Completing this, he decided to learn about architectural ironmongery, joined another business specialising in that trade and, at twenty-three, was their representative within six months, covering the north of Scotland.

Since childhood, surgery and ill health dogged his life. Hypoglycaemic attacks caused by too little sugar in the blood brought several accidents on motorways, whereby losing his licence brought about early retirement at fifty-seven, since when he took up his wish to write.

Articles, short stories and playwriting have brought him pleasure, success and a little income, but when he realised the drama in the story of the discovery of Insulin, intensive research into the behaviour of the team at Toronto University in 1922 revealed every aspect of human conduct towards each other. Dogs were used for research in the laboratories, bringing enormous elation when they lived, and bitter disappointment when they died. Controversy reigned about the findings, as did dislike and jealousy between members of the team, and frustration when their Insulin failed during clinical trials on patients in Toronto General Hospital.

Barry has given the team members 'voices', their emotions expressed dramatically through 'speaking' to each other. Some of the episodes are fictional, but 90% of the work is factual.

Ask anyone, 'Who invented Penicillin?'

'Alexander Fleming' they might answer – he was the chief discoverer but Insulin was an even greater discovery because of the millions of lives worldwide saved by its arrival. Diagnosis of diabetes was almost certainly a death sentence before 1922, so *who* discovered Insulin? Read the fascinating story in *Ezekiel's Miracle…*

PROLOGUE

Snow and ice surrounded the tarmac at Gander airport, but the blizzards that had kept the field closed for days had eased off.

The runway had been cleared and five Lockheed bombers were lined up for take-off on a transatlantic journey to England. One was to carry a passenger – not usual in winter, when flying could be hazardous. Ice forming on the wings, and the extra fuel tanks that had to be fitted, caused a weight problem.

Joe Mackey was the pilot of T9449 – one of the twin-engined planes on its way to Britain, part of the American effort to help win the war.

They were desperately needed. The bombers were straight from the plane factories. They even had the odour of cellulose paint still hanging about inside them.

Joe went across to the hangars the night before to check progress.

T9449 gleamed beneath the bright lights. A mechanic was replacing the hood over the port engine as Joe approached. He stepped down off the long ladder from the wing, pulling an oily rag from the hip pocket of his dungarees and wiping his greasy hands on it. The two were old friends.

'Hi, Mac! How's it going? Be ready for tomorrow, d'ye think?' Joe asked.

'Yeah, sure. Just fitted the new pattern oil coolers to her, otherwise she's fine.'

Joe pulled a face.

'Listen, I flew five and a half hours on Monday – that's eight hundred miles from Montreal to here, an' there was nothing wrong with the engines. I heard there'd been a couple of crashes after these things've been changed. Whose idea is this anyway?'

Mac nodded slowly. 'Yeah, I know. Trouble is, I gotta do what I'm told. It's a directive from the Lockheed people. I've got to fit them to every Hudson that comes in here. I've done a dozen this month already and they all got to England OK. Just don't worry.'

Joe walked round his charge with the mechanic, and although he did not bring up the subject of the coolers again, he was plainly uneasy.

His last comment to Mac was that he had a 'VIP' military man as a passenger. 'The Old Gent', he called him. 'He's a titled geezer – Sir Frederick Grant Banting. Goin' to some medical conference in London. Trust me to get landed with somebody like that. Don't like passengers anyway, but I'm just like you; I gotta do what I'm told.'

Mac pulled off his dungarees. 'That's me finished now. Time to shut up shop.'

Joe watched as the mechanic switched the lights off and closed the huge doors. They set off in the chill air towards the airfield buildings, lighting up cigarettes on the way, but the hangar was not empty. A narrow beam from a torch cut through the darkness. A figure emerged from a hiding place and approached the long ladder that was still in position. Making his way up to the wing and sliding open one of the canopy windows, he made his way into the flight deck. He had no right to be there…

CHAPTER 1

Alliston Simcoe County, Ontario, Canada

1898

The first day at school can be difficult for some children, and Frederick Grant Banting – Fred to all who knew him – was no exception.

He was seven when he started school, the youngest of a family of six. The school was in Alliston, two miles down the country road from Essa township. Near there lay the farm where he was born in November 1891.

Most farming families started their education at his age.

'Right, Fred. Time you were ready to get going,' his mother, Margaret Banting, called.

Fred was supposed to have got his breakfast down and be ready to leave, but there was no sign of him after leaving the table, where his brothers and sisters were still eating.

'Fred! Fred!! Come in here, wherever you are. Your father's waiting to take you in with him, but you better hurry up, or he'll go without you!'

The back door to the yard behind the farmhouse opened slowly. Fred was standing there but came no further.

'Mom, do I *have* to go to school today? I jus' don't want to go.' Margaret went over and took him by the hand. 'Your Pa won't want to hear you say that. Come on now. You're seven years old and you're a big boy now.'

Fred came forward. His mother straightened up his jacket, made sure the sandwich box was in his satchel, and led him out to where his father was sitting astride Sue, the horse he reserved for himself. Bending down, he lifted the boy up to sit in front of him.

'Come on, Son. I've got business to do in Alliston and I don't want to delay.'

Margaret waved them off and Fred, reluctantly, went to begin his education.

The classroom held a mixture of pupils: some sons and daughters of townspeople, others from the farms that surrounded Alliston. They were aged from six to eight, and taught by one teacher.

Fred took a seat near the big windows. The desk had a hinged lid with the names of former occupants picked out on the underside with pocket knives. Some he actually knew, which perked him up a little. 'If *they* can make it, so can I.'

For those attending for the first time, the teacher explained the lessons that were to come. They were basic: the three 'Rs' plus a little history and geography, both of which Fred came to like. The break was at twelve noon, when all pupils went out to the play-ground. Fred went out with another boy, a year older, from a neigh-bouring farm.

'Watch your rear,' the other boy said as Fred took the lid off his lunch box and took out an apple.

'How d'you mean?' Fred asked.

'Well, the town guys like to pick on us farm people. They'll steal your bag, throw stones at you; bullies they are. Think we're country hicks. So watch your back.'

Just with that, a group of older pupils moved over and sur-rounded them.

'That's a nice lookin' apple you got there. How's about a bite?' one said. With that, he seized Fred's wrist and twisted it until the pain made the victim let the fruit go.

'Here! That's mine. Let me have it back.'

The lad took a large bite from the apple, then threw it, with all his strength, over the playground wall. Fred turned to his new friend as the others ran away.

'Yeah. I see what you mean…'

The bullying got worse as the weeks wore on. While most of the town kids went home for lunch, too many were left for comfort. The situation developed into two camps: those who bullied the farmers' sons, and those who ran way. Fred was one of the latter.

'Please, Miss,' he said, stopping at the teacher's desk one day when the bell rang for the break. She looked up, unsmiling. 'Can I stay in school for the lunchtime? I'll sit at my desk and study something.'

'No you can't,' she replied. 'That's not allowed. You are supposed to be outside getting fresh air, not sitting about indoors.'

A year on, and the teacher had decided that Fred was not a good pupil at reading and writing, and particularly bad at spelling. She often bullied him in a different way to the physical harassment that some of the other pupils inflicted on him.

'Fred Banting! Stand up and read the passage on page sixteen of your book.'

The boy dreaded this. Flushed and embarrassed, his words were slow and hesitant. When he finished, he made to sit down. The teacher pounced at once.

'Stand up when I'm talking to you. Look here, your reading's terrible,' she snapped. 'The youngest in the class can do better than you. Take the book home and practise reading it there. You will repeat that page here tomorrow.'

Miserable and red-faced, Fred slumped to his seat.

His father, William, owned the hundred acres of ground surrounding the family home.

He specialised in fruit, grains and vegetables, together with a stock of shorthorn cattle, sheep and hogs. He was frequently asked for veterinary advice, always giving it willingly. As an elder in the local Wesleyan Methodist congregation, he was respected throughout the county.

The Sabbath day always passed quietly. After the services, Margaret and her husband liked to walk round the fields together. They were looking at the animals grazing there, at any signs of attention needed to any of them and, arm in arm, as was their wont, discussing the children and any problems they might be having. Obviously, one of the main points was Fred's report cards and the clear indications these had about his difficulties with English.

'Look, William, I could give him a bit of help with the spelling in the evenings,' Margaret suggested.

Her husband agreed with this, and offered to do something to improve his reading.

Every evening, the whole family sat and lay on cushions round the big log-burning stove in the parlour. It was a time that everyone in the family looked forward to – a time of enjoyment and relaxation after the day's hard work on the farm.

Their father would take a favourite book and read some chapters to his entranced audience.

He was an emotional man, and his wife would occasionally have to take the book and continue for him when his voice faltered and tears formed while trying to read particularly distressing passages.

'His reading ought not to be so bad, because of the evening sessions,' he remarked as they approached the farmhouse. 'Tell you what; I'll get copies of the one I'm using, so's he can follow the words himself.'

The plan didn't work. The teachers, eventually, gave up leaning on Fred, and concentrated on the more promising pupils.

Margaret caused another upset one evening. Her work done, she called Fred over. She was holding a pair of his sister's boots.

'Winter's coming on, and you can't do what the town kids do all summer, and that's go to school with shoes on your feet.'

All the farm youngsters went about barefoot, and most walked to Alliston and back, but the two miles to school could be a long journey for Fred in wet and icy weather. For that reason, he wore shoes in winter.

'These are brand new. Essie's got big feet and never wore them. Try them on.'

Fred was already disturbed at the very idea, but had to stick a foot out.

'Pull them on all the way,' his mother insisted.

He did as asked, buttoning them up.

They fitted perfectly.

'That's fine. Your last year's shoes are worn out. There's no point in letting these lie unused. You're the youngest in the family, so the boots can't be worn by any of the others.' His mother nodded with satisfaction. 'Put them on for school tomorrow.'

Her son looked at the footwear with horror, knowing that his tormentors would make a fool of him if they saw them.

'But, Mom! I'm twelve years old! And you can see these're for a girl. Don't make me wear them, please…'

His mother was adamant; he *had* to use them for the school journey.

Sleep did not come until Fred decided on a plan to avoid being seen with the boots.

Early the next morning, he washed, dressed, pulled the footwear on, and went down to breakfast. He made a last attempt to get shot of the offending boots.

'Mom, these are hurting my feet. Can you not get my old shoes soled? I'll pay for it out of my pocket money.'

Margaret still paid no heed to his unhappiness. She bent down and pressed her fingers round the outlines of her son's feet.

'They're a perfectly good fit, Fred. Now look here. Because money'll be saved in not having to buy new shoes for you, I'll see your Dad gives you something extra in your Saturday money every week from now on. How's that?'

The look he gave her should have told her volumes, but he was ushered out and told to make his way to Alliston without any further delay. Snow was on the fields, but as soon as he was out of sight, the route he took was not along the road, but cross country.

Arriving at Alliston, the back streets brought him to the school in a way that avoided him meeting any other pupils. First arrival in the classroom, he hooked his legs up under the desk, but sticking the position out until it was beyond bearing, he was forced to lower them.

Detection was instant. 'Smack' Godden was the current class bully. Immediately the children went out to the playground, his chant started up. 'Sissy Sissy Banting, wears his sister's boots. Sissy Sissy Banting…' On and on it went.

Never a boy to seek any kind of violence, this was a step too far when others took up the chorus. Fred rounded on the overweight bully. Facing him, he put up his fists.

'OK, Smack. Get yourself ready for a beating!'

In an instant, the children crowded round them. 'A FIGHT! A FIGHT!' The opponents squared up. Fred was frightened. Godden was a heavily built lumberjack's son, and would surely beat him if he got near enough, so skipping left and right, Fred managed to evade him for a while.

This didn't please the yelling spectators. 'Go on! Hit 'im. Lay 'im out. DO for 'im,' they shouted.

Fred shut both eyes, stepped closer, and lashed out with a clenched fist. There was a jab of pain as it hit something at the moment he had expected a blow to himself from Godden. Nothing *did* happen, and when he opened his eyes, Godden was kneeling on the ground.

His nose was bleeding, and he was 'blubbering', as Fred later described to cousin Hipwell, 'into the sleeve of his blouse'. The spectators cheered so loudly that one of the teachers came out to see what was happening.

Fred was a hero from then on. Not just a hero, but a champion, a saviour in the eyes of the smaller fry whose candy had been taken from them so often by the big bully. Godden never bothered anyone again, and as Fred also said, revelling in the adulation, 'It was the button-up boots did it. I almost liked them after that!'

Although trying hard to get used to them, the boots were still a source of trouble to Fred in later weeks. One day, he and his mother were out shopping in Alliston. They were walking along the main street, when Margaret became aware that her son was no longer beside, but very close behind her.

'Come away, Fred! What're you doing? You're a bit old to be playing hide an' seek, aren't you?'

He still remained, partly hidden by her voluminous skirts. She turned about and faced him. 'Look, just what *are* you up to?'

Shamefaced, he stared up at her.

'Mom, I *hate* these boots. I don't want anyone to see them, so I'm staying out of sight, behind you.'

She realised, at last, just how unbearable it was for the boy to be seen wearing girl's footwear. They were just passing a shoe shop at that moment.

'Right, Fred. We'll just go in here and get you a pair of shoes right now.'

When the sales assistant was about to take down a shoebox and a sheet of wrapping paper, Margaret gave her an order. 'Don't trouble with that, thanks. He'll just put them on right now. Put these old boots out. We don't want them.'

7

Fred breathed an audible sigh of relief as the assistant dumped the hated boots in a basket behind her counter.

Fred was still having a hard time with the teacher, who kept ridiculing him in front of all the other pupils if she was in a bad mood. After a particularly unpleasant episode with her, he went out at the lunch break and simply carried on home. His mother was baking in the kitchen when he came in, throwing his satchel down in a corner of the room and flinging himself down on the fireside chair.

'And what're you doing home at this time of day?' she asked, wiping floury hands on her apron.

'I've had enough, Mom. I'm not going back to school.'

She looked at him calmly. 'Now, now, Fred. You're upset. Did something happen?'

Her son related his problem. She could see tears welling in his eyes as he spoke. It was not only because of his teacher, but as older boys left, substitute bullies replaced them. Fred was being picked on again, and not many others were willing to become involved in defending him; he had always found it difficult to make friends, apart from his cousin and a few more.

'Have a fresh-made biscuit and a glass of lemonade to cool you down,' Margaret offered.

The pungent smell was enough to give anyone an appetite for her baking, but Fred shook his head. 'I'm going out to the stables. I'll give Molly a grooming.' Molly was his mother's horse, and Fred's favourite.

Soon after he disappeared, William came in.

'My, that's a rare smell, Margaret,' he said, picking up a broken piece of shortbread from the cooling tray.

'Hey! There'll be none left for tea tonight if people take them away like that,' she complained.

'Your baking would steal anybody's heart away. This biscuit's marvellous, Margaret!'

He slipped an arm round her waist, turned his head away and ate the rest of the shortbread, preventing his wife from retrieving it from him. Releasing her, he made for one of the chairs at the range, taking his pipe from the rack and filling it.

Margaret stopped her work and asked if he would like a coffee. He nodded. She poured two cups from the pot kept warm on the range and sat down opposite her husband.

'We have a problem, William,' she began, and told him of Fred's early return and his announcement. He lit the pipe with a taper and puffed at it while she talked.

'Where is he just now?' he asked. Just with that, Fred appeared. He had not been aware that his father was sitting quietly in the chair, and looked apprehensively at him.

If he had been expecting a rumpus, he did not get it.

William took a draw at his pipe. 'Come and sit over here, Son. I hear you've decided to give up your education?'

Stealing a glance at Fred, he noticed his face was red and when he spoke, Fred's voice was strained.

'I… I hate school, Dad. I just want to come and work with you on the farm. Plenty of the others at school have left to do that, and I'd work hard – really hard!'

William took the pipe from his lips.

'Well now, that's fine with me. We need an extra man to help in the spring, and there's plenty of work to be done, believe me. It's too bad you can never be more useful in the world than as a labourer, but a good, honest worker's all right. Think it over and in the meantime, put on your overalls and clean out the hen house.' Fred flushed even more deeply. 'But, Dad! It's not my turn!'

His father stared at him until Fred had to look away. 'It'll be your turn all the time for the foreseeable future, Fred. That's the kind of job a labourer gets to do…'

Life on the Banting farm was hard. Each member of the family who was old enough to do work had an allocated chore. One that was done on a rota basis was the cleaning out of the hen house, a smelly task that nobody liked.

The boy looked utterly miserable as he left the kitchen to go and start the job.

'You'd better put boots on, Fred,' his father called after him. 'It's a right mucky job.'

Margaret looked over to William as Fred disappeared.

'That's a bit hard on him, don't you think?'

'No, I don't think so. Just wait and see.'

Fred reappeared with his school satchel at breakfast the next day. Making no comment to the others, he ate in silence, then rose to take his departure.

'Can I get my lunch box, Mom, please.'

His mother handed him the tin box that was ready as usual.

'I see you made a good job of the hen house, Fred. Your father said to tell you that if you were back at school today, you'd take your turn with the others again, as before.'

Fred straightened up and, brightening perceptibly, shouldered the satchel.

'Gee, thanks, Mom. I'm sorry about yesterday.' As he put his hand on the door, he turned and looked at his mother.

'I don't really want to finish up as a labourer...'

* * *

1906

The town of Alliston, while small, was a busy place, its main street in the late afternoon usually thronged with shoppers, farmers, workers and school pupils. There were some tall buildings and one, several storeys high, had wooden scaffolding erected from pavement to roof level, where two workmen were doing repairs. They were on the topmost staging.

A teenager now, Fred Banting stopped to watch them from the opposite side of the street. He was on his way to meet his cousin and school friend, Frederick Hipwell, at the local drug store owned by Hipwell senior. As he stood there, he heard a creaking noise, then cracking sounds like pistol shots. Paralysed at the sight and unable to do anything, he saw the lower timbers begin to bulge outwards.

They were splitting and as he watched, the men far above turned round and, realising what was happening, made for the ladders secured to the uprights. They began to climb down, but had no chance. The ladders, with the workmen clinging to them, disappeared in the cloud of dust and debris that piled up on the dirt road in front of the building.

Young Banting kept his wits about him. He took to his heels, knowing that the workmen must be either dead or seriously injured and that there was a doctor's office round the corner.

He was lucky; the doctor was in, standing in the waiting room talking with the receptionist when the tall figure dressed in a peaked baseball cap and knickerbockers ran in. As soon as the breathless youth told him what had happened, the doctor acted at once.

'Right. I'll put some stuff in my bag and come right now. You can come and show me where the men are, and I might need you to help.'

Fred had not long to wait; it took only a couple of minutes to reach the site. Already there was a crowd of onlookers, drawing back as the doctor arrived.

Soon after this, the boy was able to continue on his way. His cousin was seated at the counter, impatient and looking for his friend.

'Where've you been? I'd begun to think you weren't coming…'

The drug store was a popular place with teenagers; the two boys met there after school to have a sasparilla or lemonade while talking about everything under the sun: sports, girls, pocket money, ambitions…

Fixed up with their drinks and sitting on tall stools at the counter, it was plain to Hipwell that his cousin was flushed and excited about something.

'Are you all right, Fred? You've got a red face and you're out of breath.'

Ignoring his drink, Fred told his cousin about the event up to the point when he fetched the doctor.

'I heard the workmen screaming as they were carried down to the ground, still holding on to the ladders, then nothing after the heavy timbers fell on top of them. It was terrible. The doctor asked me to go with him, back to the site. Already there was quite a crowd. He asked where I thought the men might be, and I was able to point to a particular place in the pile of wreckage. There were some men watching, so the doctor told them to lift the wood away.

'Sure enough, one was there all right. He was unconscious and his legs were broken. You could see that 'cos they were folded in a strange way underneath him.

'I was fairly sure where the other man lay, but he suddenly started yelling. He was covered with blood, but was able to be helped out onto the street.

The doctor asked me to run back to the surgery and ask the nurse there to telephone for an ambulance.'

Hipwell was obviously impressed. 'Wow!' was all he could say.

'It'll likely get a write-up in the newspaper tomorrow,' Frederick said, more calmly.

They bought another drink each.

'What're you gonna tell your folks?' his cousin enquired, mainly because he couldn't think of anything else to say.

'What'm I gonna tell them? I'll tell you what I'll tell them. I'm gonna be a doctor, that's what.'

'But they want you to be a minister, don't they?' his friend remarked.

'Yeah, that's true, but what I saw today, the way the doctor dressed their cuts and splinted the broken legs… gee, I just know that's what I'd like to be able to do. He asked me to pass instruments and bandages out of his bag, help the injured man out of the wreckage and lay him on the pavement until the ambulance came. I'm gonna try real hard to get to university and study medicine. My mind's made up.'

CHAPTER 2

Fred Banting kept a diary – an unusual ploy for a farmer's son.

The scaffolding accident was fully written up, as was the career decision that followed it.

The entire family faithfully attended the Methodist chapel in Alliston every Sunday.

Bible readings were given every morning before breakfast at their home, and it was the intention that Fred would enter the ministry.

The day Fred came home from Alliston to relate to his parents what had happened, William and Margaret heard the story with pride because of the quick thinking their son had displayed.

He hesitated before launching into saying what he wanted to do in the future, but plucked up courage and started off.

'I have to tell you something. You may not like what I'm going to say, but my mind's made up,' he began, defensively. 'You would like me to become a minister, but what I saw today shook me deeply. I was sure that we would uncover dead men when we took the baulks of timber off them. The first one, I thought, *was* dead, but the doctor handled him so carefully, spoke to him so gently as he came round… I just wanted to be more help, take part more fully… my whole being longed to know more about healing people.

So I've decided I'd like to become a doctor. I think cousin Frederick wants to do that too.'

William and Margaret heard this in silence. Their eyes met for a few moments, then his father spoke.

'We had hopes for a career a bit different to medicine, Fred, but I think your mother would agree that if this is what you want to do, then so be it. It's a stiff career to pursue. You'll have to do well at school to get to university, and work even harder there, but you have it in you, so go ahead. You have our blessing.'

Fred told his cousin at their next drug store conference how reasonable his parents had been when told of his ambition.

'I thought they'd go off like fireworks, but they were quite calm about it.'

Frederick took a swig of his drink. 'Well, I've spoken to my folks too. I'd like to do what *you* want, too. They're quite pleased. After all, my father's a pharmacist and that's pretty close to being a doctor, so it looks like you and me'll be together in the future. How about that?'

'Shake on it!' Fred said firmly. They gripped each other's hand vigorously.

'Let's drink on it too!' They drained their glasses.

Boys of farming stock seldom bothered about going on to high school, let alone university.

Only a small number from the Alliston area made the latter. Their local communities considered them elite, highly intelligent, and held them in awe.

The two cousins got through to the high school, and then Fred found the going increasingly difficult. His conversation with Frederick after the junior matriculation exams was singularly depressing.

'I've to resit the English Composition paper. It was my spelling and grammar that did it for me. I just can't master them, but I'm determined to pass it.'

The following year, 1909, he scraped through Latin, failed French and, once more, English Composition. William and Margaret did their best to support him.

'D'you not think that you might be better aiming at teaching, or maybe the ministry, Fred?' his mother asked.

He replied carefully. 'I think they may have to be thought about, but I'm still sure that my future lies in healing. I know it'll be an uphill struggle, but I'll make it if I just try a bit harder…'

Constantly, in his mind's eye, he saw again the scene in Alliston, and the thrill that coursed through him as he watched the doctor dealing with the injured men. Each time Fred recalled it, determination replaced any lack of uncertainty that his ambition could be achieved.

There came a day when Fred's journey home from the high school was made at a run.

Bursting into the big kitchen, he seized his mother's arms and took her on a gyrating jig round and round the table.

'Fred! Fred! What d'you think you're doing? Let go! Slow down!'

He stopped long enough to tell her the reason for his mad dance.

'I've passed everything! Passed! Passed! Passed! Even that rotten English Composition!'

Starting off the jig again, he stood on his mother's toes as she forced him into a corner of the kitchen. Red-faced and breathless, she managed to remonstrate.

'Fred! If you were a doctor right now, I'd need you to bandage my feet.'

The way was now open to enrol at Toronto University.

William, Margaret and the family gathered that weekend for a celebration. The table was laden with food, cakes and biscuits – products of Margaret's culinary skills. As the meal drew to end, William stood up to make a short speech.

'You've done well, Fred, and we all want to say how much we think of you and your success so far. You need a break from all the studies, so I've something here that'll let you do a bit of travelling to places you've never been. Here's a round-trip rail ticket that'll take you anywhere in the Canadian West. Enjoy your tour.'

Fred, sitting next to his father, rose to give an acknowledgement, but emotion overtook him. 'Gee, thanks…' was as far as he got.

'Cousin Hipwell's going with me too,' he said later. 'He's going to spend a working holiday on a relative's farm.'

The huge engine pulled into Alliston station with a hiss of steam, and carriage doors swung open. The two boys flung their cases into one, and clambered up to find that they had it to themselves. There was a blast on the engine's whistle as the train moved out.

The great adventure had begun. Neither of them had ever been further than Alliston before.

Frederick was going as far as Winnipeg, Fred to Calgary, so they were together for the first part of the journey.

'What are you going to do?' Frederick asked.

'Well, my Paw gave only a little money to me, so I'll need to find a job for a time to raise the funds a bit. Calgary's a big place, I'm told, so I'm sure I'll be OK.'

Fred's diary had quite a number of interesting entries after the train arrived at five the next morning.

Found a job digging trenches on a flower farm before seven. Not great pay, but enough to start with. '15-cent Chinese meals didn't do me any good at all… had to take a couple of days off. Travelled on to Edmonton. Got a hotel room for 50 cents a night.

Some girls in the rooms above came out on to their balcony during the night. Made a lot of racket giggling and chattering. A shifty-eyed character spoke to me next evening… asked if I wanted to 'Go upstairs.' I'll never visit such a place again.

I know a farmer who used to live in Alliston, runs a place in Saskatoon. Think I'll move on there.

All summer, he rode on the binder, stacked wheat and ate himself to a standstill.

The welcome given when he appeared back home was a happy

one, coupled with amazement because of the weight he had put on.

'You look quite different, Fred,' his father remarked.

'And the tan…' his mother added. 'What happens now,' she asked.

'I have to enrol for the General Arts course at Victoria College at Toronto University,' he answered.

'Then it's back to the grindstone…' William murmured.

1911

Victoria College had the reputation of being the best and largest centre of education in Canada.

The two twenty-year-olds – Hipwell and Banting – had their Alliston minister with them: the Reverend Peter Addison. He was familiar with the college as a former pupil himself, and able to show the boys round the various departments and lecture halls before bidding them farewell.

They walked back to the station with him, then stopped to take stock of the city they were to live in for the next few years. It had a population of around half a million people.

'Holy smoke!' Frederick exclaimed. 'Look at these motor cars! Have you ever seen so many people on the sidewalks? The shops… they're full of lovely things…'

He was gazing at some jewellery in the display windows next to where they were standing.

The two young men roomed together, sang in the 'Glee Club', studied hard, and occasionally dated a girl. Lack of money prevented the last from being anything more than *very* occasional!

Fred came down badly that first year and had to repeat several subjects. As before, English was one.

In their rooms, after the results were pasted up, Fred was so depressed that his cousin could scarcely get a word out of him. The smell of coffee permeated the air as Frederick made a pot of it on a tiny paraffin cooker in a corner. Setting a steaming beaker in front of his friend, he did his best to draw him out of his grey cloud.

'Here. Get this down you and cheer up, Fred. It's not the end of the world. You can try again, can't you?'

'Yes, I suppose so.' Taking a sip without thinking, he jumped as the coffee burned his tongue. 'But there's maybe a chance for me yet. The rules don't allow students to apply for places in the Medical Faculty unless they've full passes in all subjects. But evidently they'll let what's called "special cases" ask for special dispensations. I hardly dare ask, 'cos my exam results are pretty grim, but I'm going to try.'

His cousin smiled at him. 'Of course you should. If you do get in, you'll be well on the way, but it'll mean hard cramming, but you can do it, Fred. If anybody can, *you* can!'

Frederick was studying quietly, when a flushed Fred burst into their rooms. He was brandishing a couple of sheets of paper.

'I've made it!' he shouted. 'They've accepted my application. I'll start next session.'

When the two examined the documents more fully, it emerged that Fred would have to pick up his failed Arts course in addition to his studies in Medicine.

'I don't care HOW much work it'll take. If that's the only way I can practise medicine, I'll do it.'

CHAPTER 3

1912

The spring was sunny and warm.

Fred Banting's outlook on life was sunny too.

His medical degree course was not due to start until September, so his father and mother were pleased that he was available to work for a spell on the land. It was also the year of his twenty-first birthday.

In the Banting family, this was the time when the sons looked forward, not only to their coming of age, but to the gift from their father of a pony and buggy, fifteen hundred dollars and a fair-sized sum in back pay. This was made up with part of their wages kept back for the special occasion.

Fred took the buggy over to cousin Hipwell to show it off. The young men walked round the smart little trap, admiring its freshly painted wheels and the leather upholstery.

The pony nodded its head to them, looking for a titbit. They tied the halter to the rail and went to sit in winged wicker chairs on the veranda of the Hipwell house. Fred began by putting his plans into words as Mrs Hipwell brought glasses of cool lemonade out to them.

'We'll probably both be with the same lecturers. I believe they put people from the same district together. I've enough money to pay the fees at the university and my keep. There's the pay I'll get next summer too.

'How about boarding in Toronto where we were before at the Grenville Street rooms, if that's OK with you. It's a comfortable place and the food's good. We'll not find a better deal at five dollars a week than we get there.'

Hipwell nodded. 'That's fine with me, Fred. By the way, you

weren't half lucky to get your petition accepted. I'm looking forward to us being together in the medical studies.'

Fred grew serious. 'I'll have to work my butt off to make the arts subjects I failed last year, with the degree course as well.'

But Frederick knew his cousin's capacity for work. 'You'll get there. Just keep your nose in your books. Are you to be working at home all summer?'

'Yeah. I can earn good money there and I get more food than I can eat. Especially, I like dealing with animals, and there're plenty of them around our farm. The only thing I don't like is cleaning out the hen house and the stables, but we all have to take a turn.'

'What about Isabel?' Frederick enquired. Isabel Knight was the daughter of a bank owner in Alliston, a pretty girl much sought after by the young men in the area. She and Fred had been 'going out' together for some time.

'Yeah, well... I sure like her a lot, but it's early days yet. We'll just have to take things as they come.'

The couple continued to date for a few more weeks, until another girl caught Fred's eye at the Methodist church service one morning. Her minister father had been appointed to cover the west Essa circuit, and the family had moved to Alliston.

Several Sundays passed before he plucked up courage enough to speak to them. The congregation usually gathered in chatty groups just outside the main door when the service ended, and the girl and her mother were just moving away when Fred walked over and confronted them.

'My name's Frederick Banting – Fred to my family – and I know you are strangers in the district. I hope you don't mind my speaking to you, but we like to welcome newcomers.'

The older woman turned, smiled and replied, 'How very kind! Our name is Roach, and this is our daughter Edith. My husband is just having a word with a couple over there. If you wait a moment, he'll be with us and you can introduce yourself to him.'

Fred had already noticed this. 'The people he's chatting to are my parents, William and Margaret. We farm nearby and I'm sure they'll be arranging a visit to our home soon. Are you enjoying living in Alliston?'

It was a rather formal approach, but Fred had created a favourable first impression. He was tall. A mop of wavy hair crowned a clean-shaven face – a rather long face, almost horsy, Mrs Roach thought, but his eyes twinkled above a broad and engaging smile. She knew perfectly well that Edith was the person that the pleasant young man was interested in, and diplomatically stepped away to have a word with another woman nearby.

Edith was shy. She coloured a little and so did Fred, but they took an instant liking to one another. He murmured something about taking her on a tour of the county, if she would like to.

'That's my buggy over there,' he said, pointing to the row of tethered ponies and horses patiently waiting their owners.

Mrs Roach returned with her husband, and more pleasantries were exchanged as they parted.

The following weekend, the pony got an extra-special grooming and the trap had a mirror shine. Edith had agreed to an outing – a picnic with Fred. As he handed her up into the trap, he noticed she had nice legs… Almost as tall as Fred, clear skinned and dark haired, she also had a splendid figure.

They headed out to Simcoe County, where there were plenty of spots for picnics; drew up in the shade of some trees; and lifted out the basket of food that Fred's mother had made up for them. By then, Edith was more relaxed and easy to talk to. Over the trip round the countryside they discussed their plans for the future.

'I'm studying modern languages,' she said when the young man asked what were her interests.

'At Toronto University?' Fred queried.

'Why, yes,' she replied.

Fred's heart missed a beat.

'Well, there's a thing. That's where I'll be reading Medicine. Where're you staying?'

'I've an aunt in Church Street,' she said. Church Street was a short walk from the rooms in Grenville Street where Fred, Hipwell and another student – Sam Graham were going to live.

When the university term began, much of Fred's cramming was done with Edith at her aunt's home, where he was always made welcome. Before long, Edith discovered some of his problems, notably his spelling.

'Look, Fred; if you write prescriptions in a hand like that, I don't know how the dispenser will ever be able to make them up. Your patients will die while he deciphers them! Let's see what we can do about it.'

Fred realised only too well how badly he needed to do better. If he were to be working at the same table, close to Edith, he was entirely happy to accept her help. 'English doesn't matter quite so much as it did at the high school, but there *are* papers I have to write up on particular subjects. If you can do a bit of tutoring with my writing, I'm sure I'll be able to get through all right.'

Edith was patient and her influence good. Apart from the studies, Fred could also sense her perfume when her head was next to his. There were times when his senses began to reel…

The examination results improved from narrow passes to good 'A' grades. He was a hard worker, spending far longer over his books than the others.

When Sam and Hipwell returned after a night out, Fred was usually to be found at his desk, poring over some massive tome. When asked to join them, his answer was always the same.

'I gotta get through the subjects I failed last year. There'll not be another chance.'

Spending so much time with Edith, it was no surprise that their relationship grew deeper and deeper.

'If it wasn't for you and your help with my English,' he said, as pass marks became better, 'I couldn't possibly do so well in these exams.'

'Don't overdo it, Fred,' Edith said, tenderly. 'You're getting thin and white.'

Miss Roach was beginning to have a deep and lasting influence in Frederick Banting's life

1914

The second-year results had been pinned up on the university notice board. There was a crowd of students surrounding it, and Fred had to use his elbows to get near enough to read it.

His name was there. Passes in all subjects! His breath caught when he saw it.

Hurrying back to Grenville Street, he found the rooms empty. Sam appeared next with Hipwell.

Their faces told Fred that they too had achieved success.

'We've made it!' Fred said. 'Look, let's go out and get some booze to celebrate with.

'Prohibition hasn't stopped drinking - look at that history lecturer, the young fellow. He's permanently pickled in alcohol before he even arrives at the lecture room! I know where we can go. There's a speakeasy near the college.'

The three men linked arms and made off down the street. They were more than a little unsteady on their legs on the return...

The summer vacation started the next day. Packing quickly, the two cousins bid goodbye to Sam.

Meeting Edith at the station, the cousins found the journey to Alliston pleasant, with so much to talk about. Fred's sister was waiting with the buggy at the home station with his favourite pony,

Molly, between the shafts. The well-groomed little mare turned her head and got a hug and a pat from Fred. She whinnied just then, rubbing her soft mouth against Fred's pocket, looking for a sugar lump.

'She talks, y'know,' he told the others. 'We used to have long conversations before I left home, and she's congratulating me now.' He gave a gentle rub up and down her face with his knuckle. 'Sorry, Molly. I haven't any sugar lumps in my pocket, but you'll get one as soon as we get home.'

Mr Hipwell took Frederick and Edith off in his trap, taking them to their homes in Alliston.

* * *

During the past term, Fred had taken a night or two off his studies. Edith and he had adopted the latest craze in Toronto – ice-skating. With his arm around her waist, they skimmed around the ice rink for hours at a time, sometimes joined by other enthusiasts from the university.

They were becoming inseparable. For a change, they occasionally went dancing, but their steps were awkward and clumsy. Dancing was frowned upon by the Methodists back home, but they persevered, finding the dreamy, special closeness that dancing brings to lovers.

Their appearance, arm in arm, at church on the Sunday of their return caused quite a stir. They made a handsome couple. Tongues wagged as to how soon an engagement might be announced. Edith's parents were happy with their daughter's deepening friendship with young Banting, but there were increasing concerns over the news about the troubles in Europe. Although Britain and Germany were far away, many realised that the Commonwealth would be expected to take part in any conflagration. Canadian sons might soon be called to active service. Life went on as usual, but there was an undercurrent of worry.

The Alliston students returned to Toronto in the autumn. One evening, Fred, cousin Hipwell, Sam, Edith and their landlady's daughter Mabel, decided to go to the 25-cent Sunday supper offered by the 'Philatea Bible Class'. This was at the St James Square Presbyterian Church, not far from the young men's lodgings.

The three boys were in the University Cadets, where smart red uniforms were provided.

Fred made a suggestion before leaving. 'Let's put our cadet outfits on. My suit's needing pressed and my shirt's a bit crumpled.'

They appeared shortly after, wearing neat tunics and black trousers. Hooking arms with the girls, they set off, proudly in step, to the church hall.

Twenty-five cents bought them as much food as could be consumed, and they all did justice to the stacked plates put down to them. The usual practice was to go to the service held in the church afterwards and have a sleep during it. That did not happen this time.

An announcement was made from the pulpit that Britain had declared war on Germany.

The minister must have seen the boys and, in a lengthy and fervent prayer, asked so as to 'the Lord bless those in uniform here with us in church…'

* * *

'Let's join up!'

Fred, Hipwell and Sam all went along to the recruiting offices in August 1914. Without thinking, Fred kept his glasses on. The sergeant behind the desk asked if he had eyesight trouble.

'Certainly not! I only wear glasses for reading, Sir.'

He was failed for short-sightedness. The others were accepted without trouble, and returned to Grenville Street with a very depressed Fred.

'What am I gonna do without you lot?' he groaned.

'It'll be a while before we're called. Another few months and you can try again, Fred,' Sam declared.

The third year of studies seemed interminable to Fred, but early in 1915 he tried again.

The slaughter was well underway in France; those arriving at the recruiting stations were accepted much more readily than the year before.

'So you want to take the King's shilling, do you?' the officer asked. 'Step over to the medic and let him have a look at you.'

The examination was cursory and the doctor signalled Fred back to the officer, nodding to him as he completed the form headed 'Banting, Frederick Grant'. The box at the foot read 'A1'.

When he arrived home again, it was not to the usual cheerful welcome. His parents were sad and apprehensive. Everyone knew what was happening in France; several local lads had been killed already.

Optimists who claimed that the war would be over by Christmas of 1914 had fallen silent. The Bantings were a close family and they were all concerned about their youngest going off to war. He looked so smart in his uniform, but it was impossible for William and Margaret, his brothers, sisters and, more especially, Edith Roach, not to be worried.

His letters to Edith told of square bashing and bullying by sergeants on the parade ground.

'We trainees are all at a camp near Niagara Falls,' he wrote. 'I've been promoted already – the squaddies have to salute me now! I miss you terribly, Edith, but I'll be home soon.'

In the summer of 1915, he was back in Toronto.

'I'm to report to an army hospital, and will be able to complete my fourth-year studies whenever duties allow.'

It was not possible to see Edith so often, as leaves were infrequent and the hospital busy, but their hopes for the future centred on marriage as soon as possible. Edith continued her studies, now firm in her intentions of a career in teaching.

At one of their occasional meetings, an important discussion took place. Fred took Edith out in the trap. He had quite a lot to tell her.

'The university has decided to condense their fifth year by intensifying the course so that it finishes in the summer of 1916. I'm a bit worried that this fifth year's been shortened too much. I want to concentrate on surgery, but there's been precious little of that so far.

'Mind you, I *did* operate on a chap who had a big quinsy in his throat. He was worried about it stopping him from going overseas with his unit. The officer in charge suggested I operate and drain the thing. I was sure I could manage. I found a textbook that explained how to lance it. When I'd finished cutting there was a lot of discharge, blood and pus. I was worried stiff in case the man had a haemorrhage, but he fell asleep and didn't wake up until the next morning. I spent the night in a chair at his bedside too, but he was OK and went off with his unit forty-eight hours later. Nobody at the hospital asked if I was qualified to do such a thing. It was quite an experience, I can tell you!'

Edith heard him out in silence until the story was finished. 'Don't tell my parents in such detail, Fred. They have no idea of what happens during surgery like that, and you *do* tell the tale with all the gory bits in.'

Fred just grinned at her.

Later, Fred told Hipwell the same story again. Lifting a pint of beer, Hipwell raised his glass towards Fred. 'Well done! It must have been a bit nerve-racking. If anything had gone wrong, you'd have been in serious trouble…'

'Well, nothing did go wrong, so cheer up! By the way, I've been transferred to the Toronto Sick Children's Hospital. I've been told the man I'll be working under is Doctor C. L. Starr. He's got a good name, so I've been lucky again. I just want to qualify, see some action in France, come back and set up as a surgeon somewhere.'

1916

The finals took place in October. Fred passed with flying colours. The straightforward examinations set by the College of Physicians and Surgeons in Ontario presented no problems, and he was now entitled to practise medicine.

When Edith and he met during a few days' leave, she smiled with delight as they embraced. 'So now you are Doctor Frederick Banting! With "MB" after it, too! How *did* you manage it?'

Fred took her hand. 'Because you gave me help, that's why. I think about you so much when I'm away…'

The girl sensed an urgency in his voice as he continued.

'Edith, I think we should get engaged. The odds are that medical men will be sent off to deal with the injured troops, probably at the front. We can get married once this is all over, but the way things are going, that may be some time. I love you, Edith. I want you and I'm asking if you'll marry me. Say yes… please say yes. I've got a ring here. Will you wear it for me?'

Her eyes filled with tears as she answered, 'Of course I will, Fred. You've worked so hard, you deserve something better than the army can give you. We hear such terrible stories. The papers are full of them. Please… please… come back safe.

'I'll be all right. Just write to me often. I'll do that too, whenever I can.'

He flipped the little box open to reveal the ring. Diamonds glittered and sparkled in a nest of purple velvet.

'I've had it engraved with our initials.'

After she had looked at the scrolled lettering, he put it on her finger and moved closer to kiss her.

She returned it passionately, and Fred put his hand on her hip, moving it upwards to caress her breast. Gently, but firmly, she drew it away.

'Not just yet, Fred.' The Methodist view of anything to do with sexuality prevented her allowing him to go too far too soon…

'It's a lovely ring, Fred. I'll think of you every time I look at it.'

'Edith, you know I've had other girlfriends, but never anyone I really thought the world of. Some of the army boys who've had to leave the district got engaged too, but their girls broke away, couldn't wait. You know there's only one for me and that's you.

I'll come back, but I need to know you'll be here waiting for me. Promise you will.'

'I'll be here, Fred. And I *will* write often.'

On 6 March Fred got his final promotion, as was the pattern for all officers about to leave for the conflict. Captain Frederick Banting MB sailed from Halifax, Nova Scotia, for Great Britain and the war in the spring of 1917.

* * *

The barracks in London for the Canadians was a cold, cheerless place. The officers spent much of the time sightseeing and drinking in the mess room. Fred met his batman for the first time there.

There was no such thing as Prohibition in Britain, and Fred had been enjoying a drink when a khaki-clad figure confronted him and came smartly to attention in the corridor outside the Officers' Mess.

'Kells, Sir. Private James Kells. I'm to look after you, Sir.'

'Ah yes; well… stand at ease, Kells. D'you know where I'm quartered?'

Jimmy Kells was to be with the captain in France, where the two became friends rather than officer and batman. He was to prove an extremely good friend indeed.

A few days later an official-looking envelope arrived addressed to 'Captain Frederick Banting'. It contained a posting to Granville

Special Hospital in the coastal port of Ramsgate.

Fred and Kells took the train there the next day. Kells carried Fred's bags up some steps to a building which had a sign nailed above the doorway. It read GRANVILLE, and below it, partially obscured, was the word HOTEL.

The whole row of buildings, formerly boarding houses and hotels, had been commandeered for use as a medical centre for Canadian wounded.

Doctor C.L. Starr himself welcomed Banting.

'Well now Doctor, I'm pleased you've arrived. I'm needing all the help I can get. Come along to my office and I'll tell you a bit about our work here. You did well when you were with me as a student at Toronto Sick Children's Hospital. I've had good reports about you since then. You'll find what happens here a bit different, much more specialised… Take a seat.'

Banting cleared papers from the seat of the only chair he could see, and waited for Starr to continue.

'Wounds often sever nerves, and this can disable the patient for life. Our speciality is trying to rejoin these nerves and sinews by suturing them, along with some pretty delicate surgery.'

Banting tried to concentrate, as he was certainly anxious to specialise in just such work, but he was tired and found himself nodding. Starr noticed his eyelids drooping.

'Tell you what. You go and get settled into your rooms, have something to eat in the mess, then come back, and I'll tell you the rest. If I'm not here, get someone to find me either in the wards or in theatre.'

Banting did as he was told. He and Kells were directed to rooms upstairs. The accommodation was basic but adequate. After tidying the kit away, Kells was sent to explore the town of Ramsgate while Fred returned to Starr's office. He was still there.

'Right. To continue… The patients sometimes take a long time to recover. In some ways, we have to let nature do the major part;

we are merely helping nature to find a healing pathway. You can assist me in theatre one day very soon, then you'll see just what we're up to. Things have come a long way since men who had lost limbs were sent home with wooden legs, or stumps just stitched up. By the way, look out of the window there. On a clear day you can see France on the horizon, and we often hear artillery fire. Don't mistake the sound for thunder. It sounds like it sometimes.'

After the interview, Fred went back to his room to write letters.

Edith and his parents came first, then, surprisingly, one to his very first girlfriend, Isabel Knight.

'You will be surprised to hear from me, but this is for your father and mother too and not all for yourself. The last two months have been very long, but things should move much faster now. I may add that it cannot be too fast until I get back to Canada again. I will be very glad to hear from you any time.'

Time *did* drag, however. Thirteen months passed, during which the Granville Hospital was moved to a new site at Buxton in Derbyshire. Doctor Starr was highly impressed with his new assistant's skill in the operating theatre.

While the days passed, Edith and parents Margaret and William received regular letters from Fred, and so, strangely enough, did Isabel…

In January 1918 came one. 'I am looking after 125 patients, assisting at operations three mornings a week and being 'doctor' to about a dozen families of Canadian servicemen.

'I don't charge them anything because it gives me a certain amount of pleasure in being able to help them, which repays me more than money ever could. I was at a home last night that I wish you could have seen. A sick mother, two children already and another soon, not many comforts and no money.

'But such things teach us what good can do, and I came back quite happy in myself, tho' with a feeling of pity.'

He added, 'I think you had better train for nursing and let music and art go for some things more real…'

At this stage, time was hanging on Fred's hands. Some of the young nurses at the hospital were fair game for a handsome officer like Captain Banting. Some of them began to receive quite expensive gifts from him. One in particular was the pretty daughter of Fred's boss, Doctor Starr.

She arrived at the office one day, when Banting was alone there, writing up case notes.

'Doctor Banting. A word with you please,' she said, rather sharply.

Fred sat back and pushed the papers away. 'Well, hello there. How nice of you to come.'

She laid a package down on the desk. 'This isn't a social call. Look here! You mustn't give presents like this to me – and I'm not the only nurse to have one from you. It's not the done thing at all, especially when I believe you're engaged to a girl back in Canada. You *are*, aren't you?'

Fred, red-faced, tried to persuade her to keep the gift, but she was adamant.

'If you persist in this obnoxious behaviour, I'll have no alternative but to report you to my father. It must stop. You'd be better getting on with your job and keeping away from the female staff.' She turned and stalked away, leaving Fred speechless, hot and even more red-faced.

The next letter to Isabel made an oblique reference to the situation.

'I don't know what I would do if I were not busy,' he wrote. 'For getting something done keeps one out of trouble – the latter is inclined to present itself rather often over here…'

William and Margaret Banting back in Alliston learned that he had decided to try for a Fellowship of the Royal College of Surgeons in England.

Before this could be attempted, they were told of his imminent departure for France.

'I have orders to report for embarkation next week. I'll have to give up my studies. I'd rather win the Military Cross than become an FRCS anyway.'

The flippant words did not delude them. There were thousands of casualties posted every week. Many were Canadians.

It was June 1918.

CHAPTER 4

4 August 1918

All the French ports were packed with ships. Fresh-faced troops disembarked; worn-faced wounded were stretchered or helped on board. The final battle of the blood-spattered conflict was being fought along a line between Arras and Amiens. Captain Banting and Private Kells came ashore from the troopship at Dieppe. There were lorries and ambulances lined up on the quay. Derricks were lifting crates of ammunition, foodstuffs, guns and medical supplies ashore from the ships' holds. Stevedores were unloading under orders from the army officers.

'Right then, let's get these in here,' Fred Banting told Kells. Several men handed up cases marked with red crosses to the tail-board of one of the ambulances. A soldier inside dragged them away, packing them tightly together so that they would not be dislodged when the vehicle made its way over the potholed roads to the clearing station at Arras, near the Belgian border.

An officer, his uniform stained and dirty, came over to Banting.

'Go in the ambulance. You'll be needed as a relief man just now. You'll find plenty to do. Clean, close and dress wounds, then send the ambulance back with the worst cases to the base hospital here. We'll look after them – get them on board ship for home. The big show's just starting, so there'll be a flood of injured men pretty soon. See you later.'

Kells swung up beside the driver and extended his arm to Banting. The three were packed uncomfortably together on the hard bench seat; there were no partitions between them. Kells' elbow stuck into Banting's ribs. The weary officer gave a half-salute as the big vehicle chugged off, red crosses clear on white backgrounds.

'Sorry, Sir. Not much room in here,' the batman yelled above the roar of the engine.

'Can't help it.' This as his elbow once more jerked into his superior's side.

'It's all right. What a mess!' Banting replied, hanging on to a handrail beside the seat as the ambulance swayed and lurched along the pitted roadway. The holes were deep, most filled with muddy water, and it was impossible for their driver to avoid plunging into some of them. Piled along the verges were swollen bodies of horses, wrecked carts, and broken-down trucks.

'You haven't seen anything yet, Sir,' the driver told him as he held on to the bucking steering wheel, keeping the ambulance on course with difficulty.

Three and half hours later, they pulled up at a damaged farmhouse with a Red Cross flag clinging to its pole, in pouring rain. As the three men clambered stiffly down, orderlies ran forward from a barn and began to unload the boxes. As soon as this was done, they carried the wounded out to the ambulance. Kells put his arm round a man whose head was bandaged over one eye. He was using a crutch to keep a foot off the ground. Blood showed red through the layer of white cotton swathed round it.

'You'll be back in Blighty soon!' Kells said.

'Anywhere'll do as long as it's away from here!' came the reply. The batman levered the soldier up folding steps and into the vehicle.

An orderly helped the patient to a place on benches lining the sides. Others too weak to sit were laid on the floor on straw-filled palliasses, many stained red with blood. Once all the wounded were loaded, the driver set off on the return journey to Dieppe at once.

Banting joined the other doctors hard at work on injured men arriving every few minutes.

Some of the less shell shocked were able to tell a little of what was going on at the battlefront. The stories were horrifying, but few had time to listen. The best that could be done was the offer of a cigarette to those who wanted one.

The battle eased off a little, and Banting and some of the officers were able to do a little sightseeing. There was not much left of the town, and most of the remaining citizens were living in cellars below the ruins of what had been their homes.

Banting sat on his bunk one evening and began letters to home. The first was to his parents.

It gave details of some of his experiences and about the harsh conditions the infantrymen had to endure. There was news about himself too.

'I've even got a bit of time to study – about fifty pages a day just now. I was given a bottle of wine by a Frenchman today – says we're winning the war. I do hope so, then I can get back home and start up again. I'm going to be in charge as Medical Officer of the battalion, the 4th Canadian Division, from the end of this month. I'll not have time to write as there are 1000 men in the unit and there will be stretcher bearers and orderlies to look after. There will be a lot of surgery to do.'

He decided not to tell them that he would be at the front. Three weeks later, his unit was commanded to move forward.

His heart beat faster as he read the orders. The wounded brought to the farmhouse were, in many cases, terribly injured, some dying. They told of facing relentless machinegun fire, hand-to-hand fighting, bayonet charges, running over wounded soldiers pleading for help, falling into trenches full of mud and unburied corpses.

The odds of coming back unhurt lessened by the day.

One September night, heavy artillery bombardments had continued for hours from British and German guns some distance behind the lines. Star shells shed a hard, brilliant light over the barren no-man's land between the trenches. The short distance was pockmarked with craters and mounds of earth, stumps of trees, barbed wire and remains of human beings.

The 4th Battalion was to mount an attack at dawn. The sky had just begun to lighten, when a whistle blew. The men went over the top, yelling as they ran forward, to be met by a hail of machinegun bullets from the German trenches just a hundred yards ahead of them. Little flashes of yellow showed their positions through the murk. Infantrymen close to Banting threw up their arms and fell, some with a scream, some silently, dead before they hit the ground. No one on his feet stopped running for a moment. The safest thing to do was to keep moving, but there was no protection of any kind. Those who got near enough threw grenades into the trenches where grey steel helmets glinted over the barrels of guns. Eventually the Canadians dropped over the ledges, and after short hand-to-hand fighting with bayonets and revolvers, took the position. Some landed on German troops lying in the mud. Anyone still alive and wearing a grey uniform was shot.

The Canadians were trying to occupy a town called Drury. Banting and his men could see their countrymen's steel helmets bobbing along the trenches now and then, some distance ahead. Bulky shoulder bags and satchels of surgical instruments, bandages and equipment hindered the medical orderlies. From time to time, above the racket of gunfire, sniper fire made them keep down below ground level, and while none was hit, the crouched position made their passage even slower.

They came across some injured Canadian soldiers in a hollow in the road. Banting examined them and issued orders.

'Nobody's badly hurt. Dress their wounds and leave enough stretcher bearers to take them back behind the lines. The ambulances will collect them from there.'

As the party left, the wounded lying on the banking took out white clay pipes and cigarettes. They looked relaxed because they knew that for most of them, the fighting was over meantime.

Banting's men pressed on. Suddenly they came on a crowd of German prisoners being held in the remains of a barn. Three private soldiers and a corporal were guarding them. The corporal saluted as the captain approached.

'How many Germans have you there?' he asked.

'There are forty, Sir.'

'Look, I could do with some of them to help with carrying stretchers. I've had to leave some of mine behind. I'm sure nobody would miss them and they'd be doing something useful. Count twenty off. Can you speak German? If you can, tell them what I want.'

The corporal knew one of the prisoners spoke English. A column of men came forward and Banting ordered his men to partner off with them. They worked willingly, trudging through the trenches with injured British, Canadian and the occasional German, taking them back to advanced field stations. As night fell, work stopped and a roofless farmhouse provided shelter. The wearied men lay on the floor, with rolled up capes and greatcoats for pillows. The inevitable pipes and cigarettes were lit, and the air filled with smoke. One German lying near one of the Canadians spoke to him quietly. '*La guerre, pour moi, est fini…*'

'You're a lucky bastard, you are. The war may be over for you, but we're still in it…' came the reply.

The following day, the prisoners were handed over to a party of British troops returning from the front, and that was the last that Banting's squad saw of them.

Conditions at Cambrai were even worse. 'Trench foot' was all too common, caused by mud, which could reach the knees of men moving constantly along the trenches. Little could be done to treat the trouble other than keeping the feet dry, and there was seldom much chance of that. Heavy cases of ammunition, crates of food, even the injured on stretchers, all finished up in the mud at some points, joining the cursing men struggling to keep their balance in the stinking slime. Duckboards laid over the glutinous swamp helped, but not all trenches had these. It was a hell on earth, with frequent curtains of poison gas leading to the wearing of the only pathetic protection available – wet canvas sheets draped over heads and shoulders. A mica panel allowed limited vision. Some had proper masks, but a gas attack lasting several hours was not unusual.

Attention to the injured had to go on. The closer to the front, the more essential this was. Banting did not flinch, setting up any kind of place sheltered from the shelling to carry out surgery on men brought by continuous lines of bearers.

There was a point where German troops had just vacated a length of trench in which was a roomy dressing station. The Canadian attack was so fierce that the only Germans left were dead Germans. As soon as the position had been cleared, Banting and his team moved in.

'Look at this,' he said, lifting a rough canvas away from a narrow opening in the trench wall and walking inside the chamber it had covered. 'All this medical equipment… even an operating table – bit rough and ready, but it'll do. Get the first man in here and we'll start right away.'

An assistant laid out gut for stitching, scalpels, bandages and dressings. Another trimmed the wick of the lantern hanging over the table. Kells was always given the job of getting enough boiling water to sterilise instruments and clean up the men before and after surgery. He set about it with a spirit heater and a kettle. The first patient was brought in, and Banting worked steadily for twenty minutes. Once the patient was taken away, the next moved in, then another, and another… The wounds, ranging from bullet holes to limbs blown off by grenades, were dealt with steadily and efficiently for the next hour.

There was a sharp explosion just outside the dugout entrance a few seconds later.

An officer was carried in and laid on the table. A grenade had gone off just in front of him and almost amputated his foot.

It was hanging by a few strands of tissue, and a pool of blood formed on the table top where the bearers laid him. The man was fully conscious and gazed up at Banting.

'Have to come off, won't it?'

The surgeon nodded. 'You'll not feel anything after I give you an opium injection in the leg. It'll be your ticket back home…'

One of the attendants cut away the leg of the soldier's uniform and put a tourniquet above the amputation site. The soldier lay back, his face tense.

'Get on with it then.'

Banting crouched over the patient and carried out the injection. When the surgeon nodded, the assistant handed him a scalpel, and the operation began. Suddenly the officer sat up, pulling a revolver from his holster. The staff had overlooked the rule that all armaments should be removed from patients at once.

There was a figure at the low entrance – a German soldier. The man on the table pulled the trigger and a shot rang out. In the enclosed area, the sound was stunning. At point blank range, the intruder died instantly and the officer fell back, the smoking revolver falling from his hand to the floor.

The two men, concentrating on the operation, jumped as the shot rang out. They stopped momentarily, but as their patient fell back again, carried on while smoke curled round the paraffin lamp above them.

The Canadians were not aware that a solitary enemy infantry-man had managed to remain hidden further up the position and was seeking shelter anywhere. The finding of the operating theatre was, for him, a fatal discovery.

It was to take days of fierce fighting before the wreckage of

Cambrai was won.

Banting did little else but operate on men of the 4th Battalion during the initial assault on 27th September. He worked most days from ten in the morning until eleven at night, until, learning that the medical officer of another battalion, which had taken over the attack, had been hit, went across to their lines to deal with their wounded.

One evening, he was snatching a few hours' rest, when his senior officer, Major Palmer, shook the dozing surgeon's arm.

'Sorry, Banting. We'll need to reconnoitre a bit now that the front has moved on. We'll have to find a suitable place to set up new advance dressing stations nearer the centre of Cambrai. The east end of the town's clear. We'll need to go now. Are you up to it?'

Wearily, Banting got up from the camp bed that Kells had found somewhere. Pulling on his uniform jacket and gas mask case, he stood up. Handing a helmet to him, the major spoke again.

'Think you'd better take this with you. There's quite a lot of shelling going on, and there are always snipers around.'

Kells appeared behind Banting, already carrying his rifle. 'Ready, Sir?'

'Ready, Kells. Let's go.'

The batman shouldered the rifle, and the three stepped out into a grey dawn.

As they walked through the suburbs, they found the streets littered with masonry that had fallen from shattered buildings, some still burning. There were lookouts at regular intervals, watching from sandbagged posts for any movement at the gaping windows, where sharpshooters lurked. The Germans were still occupying the west side of Cambrai.

'There's a building that might suit,' Palmer said, pointing at the far side of a small square.

They had only stepped forward a few yards when the major grabbed Banting's arm.

'Take cover. Shells coming!' Kells and Palmer dived into a crater nearby and scrambled down the side. Banting was not so lucky. His choice of refuge held the remains of a putrefying donkey, and he landed on top of it. The salvo flew over them and none followed. Banting extricated himself and tried to remove some of the slimy mess from his uniform.

The stench revolted him, but when Major Palmer appeared, convulsed with laughter over his appearance, he could only join in and make the best of it. They had not long to enjoy the amusement as another burst of shelling drove them to take cover again, this time all three in one shell hole.

'You smell like a glue factory,' Palmer remarked. 'It's as well Kells will have the job of cleaning up your uniform!'

They made their way warily forward towards the large building that had caught their interest, and walked through the doorway. It had several floors, but there was a stair leading downwards to a basement.

'This has possibilities,' Kells remarked. 'Basements are always safer.' Starting off down the steps, he backed up a few seconds later.

'No good, I'm afraid. It's flooded.'

The others had found the ground floor full of rubble but were mounting the stairs to the upper floor, when Kells rejoined them. They were going to use their binoculars from the vantage point to see if there were any likely places that suited their purpose.

Banting moved over to the windows at the first floor and looked out.

'Look at this!' he exclaimed, pointing through the broken glass.

A line of cavalrymen was galloping over what had been a public park. There was a machinegun emplacement on the far side, where purple flashes showed that bullets were already flying. As some of the horsemen faltered, a few reining their mounts in, others struggled to hold their seats as terrified horses reared or fell. They turned, about to retreat, but the machinegunners cut most of them down.

'They're Russians! Who else would be so bloody stupid?' the

major exclaimed, adjusting the focus on his glasses.

Just as he steadied them on the window sill, a shell exploded close to one cavalryman, throwing horse and rider to the ground.

The animal struggled to its feet, shook its head, then went over to the soldier lying a few yards away. Thrusting its muzzle under him, the Russian began to get up, then, as the animal waited patiently, managed to remount. Even the machinegunners stopped firing at the amazing sight. Rider and horse wheeled about and galloped away, disappearing in the distance as the gunners took up their pitiless firing again.

'I can't believe this,' Banting said. 'It must be about the last cavalry charge this side of the century…'

'Best get on with this survey,' Palmer urged. 'You can't go back to our lines smelling the way you are. Even the Huns'll take to their heels if they got a whiff of you!'

Outside, over in the park, the few horses still on their feet wandered off, but not one had a rider.

Shelling began again an hour later, by which time a basement cellar had been earmarked as a dressing station. As the trio passed a low wall on their way back to the lines, a shell landed close by. Banting felt as if a cricket ball had stuck his right arm. A sharp pain followed it. An 'L' shaped piece of shrapnel had torn a jagged wound halfway between wrist and elbow. Blood was running down his hand.

'You're hit, Banting. Let's have a look. Go down there into that garden,' the major ordered.

'I'm OK,' Banting answered, holding the arm above the wound tightly to stem the bleeding.

'Look! Do what you're told. Get down behind that wall and let me take a look.'

Palmer looked at the torn flesh. One glance was enough to tell him that the wound was deep and serious.

CHAPTER 5

When Private Kells helped Captain Banting down from the ambulance at Dieppe, the same officer who had waved them off just a short time before gave them a cheery welcome.

His uniform was even more creased and stained than the last time they met.

'Well, well. That was a short holiday you've had in France!' He noticed Banting's arm bandages and the sling. 'Next booking on the Channel steamer'll be a couple of days. You'd better go along to the casualty station. You'll get a rest there and they'll check your arm.'

The two men were tired out, having made the long journey from the Belgian border by train. They had had no food other than a mug of hot tea and a roll when they stopped at a station while the engine took on water. They were fed and given beds for the night. Banting managed to write a brief note home, using his left hand, but it was legible.

'Please don't worry. I am the luckiest boy in France.'

In the morning, Kells was already up and dressed before Banting. He came into the room, fully kitted out in a clean uniform.

'Just come to say cheerio, Captain. I've been told that you'll be leaving for England tomorrow. I've been ordered back to the front today, so this is goodbye, Sir. You *will* look after yourself...'

He stuck his hand out.

Banting could manage only a few words. 'God, Kells, what am I going to do without you?'

He was never to see his batman again.

Two days later, Banting arrived at an army hospital in Manchester. The arm was in a sling, his uniform bloodstained and torn. The shrapnel had been removed at the field station in France, and the wound stitched, but it was still bleeding and painful. When the bandages were taken off, the surgeon shook his head.

'You're going to be with us a while, I'm afraid. The rest won't do you any harm anyway.'

One of the surgeons from Granville Hospital in Buxton came to see him a few weeks later.

He walked up the ward to where Banting was sitting, clad in pyjamas and a dressing gown, reading a newspaper. He was surprised and delighted to see his visitor.

'Well hello, Fred. Doctor Starr suggested I come and convey his best wishes. He wants to know first hand, how you're doing – as we all do.'

Banting indicated a chair. His smiles showed how pleased he was to have a caller from his former place of work. His visitor, Walter Gallie, had arranged with Banting's surgeon to see the wound. He was one of Fred Banting's former colleagues at the Buxton army hospital. A sister and the house surgeon came forward to meet him a few minutes later. While the two specialists discussed the case, the sister cut away the dressings and revealed the extent of the injury.

'The shrapnel bypassed the bones and there're no fractures, but it damaged the ulna and probably some nerves,' the doctor explained.

Gallie raised the arm so that he could see more closely.

'You've had a lucky escape here, have you not?' he exclaimed. 'It's possible that the nerve damage isn't all that great.'

It occurred fleetingly to Banting that he might ask for a referral to the Buxton hospital, where Starr was still specialising in just such cases as his own. About to ask Gallie if he would put in a word on his behalf, he thought the better of it. His caller had just been telling him that the hospital was overflowing with patients, many in a far worse condition than himself.

Gallie straightened up.

'I don't see any problems. You'll be all right once the wound heals over,' his visitor reassured Banting. The sister ordered a nurse to dress the wound as the house surgeon left.

The two men talked while this was done, Gallie retailing the progress that Starr was making, and suggesting that perhaps Banting might rejoin his team once his health returned. Banting told of the sights and scenes he had seen in the short time spent at the front.

'As to what I'll do after all this is done with, I really haven't thought much about it. I still have studies to complete, although I've been doing a lot of that to while away my time here,' he said as Doctor Gallie was leaving.

He had not told him that he had been passing some time with some of the pretty young nurses, even making mild passes at them, and bossing them about when senior staff members were not around. One was dressing his arm, when he drew her into conversation. 'I'm hoping to get back to active service within a couple of months,' he told her.

'We'll miss you when that happens,' she murmured, with a trace of sarcasm that Banting missed altogether…

During the ward rounds a few days after Gallie's call, the surgeon sat down closer to Banting, who was sitting with his arm resting on a pillow on the bed.

The dressings had just been removed, and neither he nor his patient liked what they saw.

His visitor had been rather over-optimistic in his diagnosis. The wound was wet and inflamed. There was pus round the edges.

'D'you think I might be discharged soon?' Fred Banting asked.

The doctor shook his head. 'I doubt that very much. You're as much an expert as I am, and you can see there's quite a bit of septicaemia there. You'll need to stay with us a while, until that's healed up.

It took until 4 December 1918 before he was discharged.

During the months of waiting in the Manchester hospital, he had an important visitor – an army officer, a colonel. Banting stood to attention as the smartly uniformed man approached. He had a neatly trimmed white moustache, and several medal ribbons.

'Stand at ease – there's no need for that here, Captain. I've come to bring you some good news. You've been awarded the Military Cross, put up for you by Major Palmer for your work in France. Here's the citation. It says your energy and pluck were of the highest order, and I'm sure you've earned it. There's an investiture at Buckingham Palace in a few weeks. I hope by then you'll be fit enough to attend?'

Banting shook hands and, in spite of being ordered not to, snapped to attention again as the colonel turned away, leaving the parchment citation face-up on the bed.

Some of the other patients and staff had gathered round as the little ceremony was performed. After a few words with them, the colonel departed and Banting was left being congratulated by everyone… especially the female staff. He loved every minute of it.

4 December 1918

The release from hospital came just three weeks after the Great War ended.

Captain Banting looked very smart in his newly pressed uniform. Although he no longer had Kells to polish his boots and carry his luggage, an orderly saw him to the foyer, where a clutch of nurses was waiting to wish him well. One or two kissed him; others giggled and chattered. It was a sad parting in a way. Two or three had entertained hopes of a relationship deeper than the harmless flirtations that had caused a few female hearts to flutter during his long stay.

'What are you going to do now?' one asked.

'I've been invited to spend some time in Edinburgh. After all, I need to recover from some of the treatment some of you girls have been giving me.'

There were shrieks of laughter at this until a staff sister came through the double doors to the vestibule and wished Banting a more formal farewell.

In Scotland, he enjoyed being wined and dined in Edinburgh.

The distinguished medical fraternity at the capital vied with each other to entertain the wounded Canadian officer who had been decorated for bravery.

The next letter to Isabel Knight told of the possibility of doing graduate work in Edinburgh, but 'time and poverty prevent this…'

One to Edith and another to his parents followed it a few days later.

'I have orders to return to the Christie Street Military Hospital in Toronto, and will sail on the *Belgic* later this month. February here is bitterly cold.'

Edith's had an addition: 'I keep warm thinking of you and how soon we can be together. We will talk about our wedding as soon as I get home.'

The ship berthed early in March, and Banting travelled to Alliston to a rapturous welcome from his parents, brothers and sisters. After eating the kind of meal that only a farmer's wife can provide, he set off with the pony and trap for the Roach home.

'My darling!' Edith, who had been watching for the buggy all afternoon, ran out from the porch. The pair embraced and hugged for some time before they parted and, hand in hand, went into the house. Edith's parents were waiting for them. The minister stepped forward to shake Fred's hand.

'We praise God that you have returned safely. Come away in and have some tea with us.'

Fred talked a lot, giving some idea of what devastation there had been in France and Germany, and how three shillings would buy a spiked officer's helmet from a starving German soldier and a girl sell herself for a loaf of bread.

Edith stole a glance at her parents. They were tight-lipped and unsmiling, even at Fred's rather crude jokes. She became more and more uncomfortable during some of the stories he was relating. Violence and horror dominated them. The scenes he was describing were aeons away from the lifestyles of a Methodist minister, the calmness of Alliston and its surrounding farms.

The gentle couple could never envisage the slaughter, the summary execution of wounded soldiers on both sides, trenches filled with mud and corpses, the towns – once lined with rows of houses – where scarcely one brick was left standing on another.

Fred Banting was no longer the amiable, soft-spoken boy who had left to go to war. He was a man now, and intent on making sure that everyone knew it.

'You'll have a great deal to talk about. We'll leave you alone, as I have other work to do,' Edith's father said, as both parents rose before Fred could start another anecdote. Her mother came round the table and gave Fred a little hug and a kiss.

'Dear Fred. I can't say how much we have all prayed for your safety. You must try to forget the terrible things you have described. We are at peace now, and we want things to return to normal. Try to think that way and about what the future holds for the two of you.'

They left the room as Edith and Fred stood up. They went through to the parlour, where comfortable furniture and a cheerful fire burning in the grate awaited them.

Edith sat on the settee. Fred joined her, took her hand, and put his arm round her waist. She moved closer and they kissed, more and more passionately. It was at that point that Edith became aware of the smell coming from her fiancé. It was of stale beer and cigarettes.

Both smoking and drinking were habits disapproved of by the Methodists, and she had also been taken aback to hear the amount of strong language that Fred was using, not only during their short conversation before coming into her home, but also in front of her parents.

She resolved to try to stop these habits as soon as possible, but this was not the time.

She settled for moving back a little from him.

'Fred... It's just wonderful to have you here. I can't tell you how happy I am to see you home again. So much has happened to you since you went away. How is the arm?'

'It took a lot longer to mend than I ever thought it would, Edith. You know I was wounded in late September last year, and because the bloody thing went bad on me, I had to stay in hospital in Manchester – it seems so far way now – until December...'

Edith winced inwardly at the swearing.

'...It gives me pain sometimes, but I can use it all right. A surgeon can't have a shaky hand, y'know, and I thank God I don't have that.'

Fred got up and sat facing her from a wicker chair opposite the settee. 'I can look at you better from here, Edith. My eyes can't take everything in – you've become even more beautiful than the picture I kept in my mind all during the war. The photograph I had with me got wet and dirty. To see the real you in front of me now... I feel... I just can't find words. And you, dear, I haven't heard about what's going on here yet. How are you enjoying working?'

Edith's mind was reeling. Fred was so ardent in his behaviour and the things he was saying.

She recovered concentration and began.

'Well, I told you in my last letter, all about my graduating with a good degree in education and winning a medal in Modern Languages... I'm teaching now and earning a good salary. I love the job.'

Fred told her that he had not received her letter. 'The mails became unreliable as the end of the war approached, so this is all news to me. I'm delighted for you, Edith. You're not only beautiful, but brainy as well...'

She talked on calmly, about the pupils, the school and its

classrooms, but there were questions she was desperate to ask. Eventually she could wait no longer.

'Fred, I'd like to get married soon and set up home somewhere. Let's talk about that. It's so important to me. I've waited so long for you, just as you begged me to do when you left, but it's been a long wait.'

Fred hesitated for a moment, holding silence as he fished in his pocket, bringing out a packet of cigarettes.

'Would your folks mind if I smoke?' he asked.

Edith put a hand on his wrist.

'I'm afraid they would, Fred. There's never been smoking by anyone at home as far back as I can remember.'

'OK, but almost everyone in the army smokes – and not only in the army either.'

The packet caught in the flap of his uniform pocket as he tried to put it back, but he crushed it in with a gesture of irritation.

'Look, Edith, I'm just as anxious as you to be married and set up home, but I've hardly any money, to start with. Servicemen don't get paid much, and when I get out from the army, probably in the summer, I've decided to complete my original training at the hospital for sick children in Toronto. Doctor Starr's back there, along with a group of up-and-coming young surgeons. Completing my apprenticeship will probably take about a year. I can probably get a post doing surgery there, and it should be possible to earn quite a decent salary that way.'

Fred did not notice that Edith's expression had changed. She did not like the way his conversation was going. He continued looking at the floor as he pressed on.

'I'll rent a house and start a practice somewhere as a surgeon and general practitioner – and that'll take a year or two to build up, so I don't see us getting married before then.'

He looked over, and was taken aback at the distress showing in her face. Already feeling disappointed at his opening remarks, she was stunned at what he was saying.

She was utterly taken aback at his suggestions; they completely destroyed the bright and rosy future she had in her mind's eye. There had been no warning whatever of his intentions in any of his letters.

'Do you mean that it's going to be at least three years before we can marry, Fred? Do you realise that since our engagement three years have passed? And now you're asking me to wait another three.' She turned white as she struggled to keep calm, not to reveal the turmoil that was hurting her so deeply. 'Fred, I realise you need to complete your training, but I'm making enough to let us start up right away as man and wife. I've been dreaming about this for ages, saving up too. There's more than most couples have to begin with.'

Fred pushed his chair back, increasing the distance between them. Frowning, he gave a sharp reply. 'There's no way I can do that. If I can't support a wife, then I don't get married, and that's that. I'd be ashamed to live the way you're suggesting.'

The life she had envisaged was certainly not what Fred intended – that was clear enough.

She had sufficient savings to buy a decent house, in Toronto if necessary, but his next remarks made it clear that he did not want her working either.

'When I can do the honourable thing and set up a practice in a good house where we can also live, then that would be ideal. The money I earn will mean you don't have to work. Few that I know who've got married have so-called "working wives", so I see us as living from *my* earnings alone. You'll find that once the family arrives, there'll be little enough time for anything else anyway.'

Once more he had trampled tactlessly through her ambitions, without discussion or thought.

Her immediate feeling was of bitterness. Her years of study – and hard study at that – the happiness in her teaching and the good salary earned, seemed of no matter to Fred; they were to be abandoned without further ado. Compromise of any kind was not in his sights.

Edith stood up and half turned away so that he would not see the resentment that she was sure was showing in her face.

'I must say I'm surprised, Fred. I love you, and I know you want me as your wife, but it seems that it can only be on your terms. All we need between us is love. It overcomes all problems, and when the only problem is that you can't meet me over my offer, then I am deeply disappointed.' Her heart was pounding. She tried to step back a little from the conflict.

'We'll need to think this out. Let's leave things for the moment.'

Fred got to his feet and came towards her, but she turned her back on him so that he could not see the tears and distress on her face.

Still with her back to him, she opened the door, called to her parents to come and bid goodbye to the visitor, and gestured Fred past her to the hall. Surprised at the young man's sudden departure and his refusal to stay for an evening meal, they could do no more than give Fred a courteous farewell. As the door closed, Edith ran upstairs to her room, leaving her parents wondering what could possibly have happened.

CHAPTER 6

The journey home was made with a heavy heart. After letting the pony, Molly, into the field to graze, she came over to the fence for the usual sugarlump, but Fred simply latched the gate, put the saddle away in the stables, and walked away into the farmhouse. He dragged himself to the chair nearest the kitchen stove, and threw himself down in it. His mother had expected him to be cheerful and elated. She saw at once that something was wrong. He looked so miserable.

'You're wearing a face, Fred. Did things not go well at Edith's?'

'Badly, I'm afraid. Very badly indeed.'

She brought a cup of tea over to him and dusted her hands on her apron before sitting down opposite her troubled son. He waved the tea away, and Margaret took it herself.

'If you don't want to talk about it, don't. Go off and see if your cousin Hipwell's in. I know he's been back from the war a while, and he'll want to see you. After Edith's, I thought he'd be your next call.'

'If Edith and I had been able to see eye to eye, it would have been; but, Mom, I really don't want to talk about it just yet. I'll go out for a walk and clear my head for a bit. I'll get some tea when I come back.'

He was away an hour, and on his return, changed from his uniform into 'civvies'.

He seemed a little brighter, but not much. Sitting down at the kitchen table, he began to tell Margaret the sad tale of his fiancée's reaction to his proposals.

Margaret Banting was a wise woman, and did not try to argue. She had sometimes felt, as her family grew up, that the kind of life she led herself was hardly likely to attract an intelligent young woman like Edith. Farmers' sons usually married farmers' daughters, and she had a family of five boys and one girl. Tradition before 1914 was always that a wife did not go out to work – she stayed home, did the housework, the cooking, raised a family and, if a farmer's wife worked, it was on the land. But when the men went off to the war, everything changed. Much of the ploughing, haymaking and potato digging was done by the women. In Britain, they manned the trams and worked in the munitions factories. All this ran through Margaret's mind as she listened to Fred.

'Things have changed a lot in the last few years' was the only comment she made, so softly that her son barely made it out.

Summer 1919

William Banting, after hearing about Fred's difficulties from Margaret, asked him to come into the parlour one evening. The storytelling sessions were no longer carried out, although Bible readings were still given at breakfast and before the family separated to go to bed. The two settled themselves into chairs after William put some more wood on the stove.

'Right, Fred. We need to talk. Have you thought about what you want to do after you leave the army? There's enough work to keep you earning some money here, but I appreciate you want to finish your training in surgery, so that's out. I would have thought you would want to get married as soon as you can, so how about I give you some money to start the general practice you've talked about and forget about the surgery? I can spare it, you know.'

Fred looked uncomfortable, and shifted in his seat.

'That's very generous, Father, but I've set my heart on surgery. After all, I did plenty of it in the army. It'd be a pity to let all that experience go for nothing, wouldn't it? Doctor Starr is back at the Sick Children's Hospital in Toronto. If I could study with him again, gain his specialist knowledge, there'll be plenty of patients who've been injured in the war. He's got a team of surgeons who are doing highly successful operations on his nerve-rejoining techniques, and *that's* what I'd like to do.'

A few days later, the mailman delivered a long envelope containing Fred's discharge from the army. It signalled the end of a short, but exciting phase in his life. For some reason, a permanent job at the Sick Children's' Hospital evaded Fred, even though he was liked by most of the staff, particularly at Starr's specialist ward. A year later, he was becoming a known figure in the treatment of infants with severe burns and shock. Starr and others in the team thought he would do well to continue in that field, but Fred's restless nature led him backwards rather than forward. Cleft palates, tonsil and adenoid removals, swallowed safety pins and the administration of anaesthetics seemed to take precedence over research into more specialised territory.

Edith and he met regularly. She found him courteous and polite – the perfect gentleman – until she disagreed with him over some trivial matter, when he would fly off the handle and lose his temper. Discussing matters with Hipwell on a visit home, he gave the reason for the predicament with Edith.

'I make money, Frederick, but I can't make enough to take her out and pay for a decent meal. My income barely pays the rent and my keep. She insists that she'll pay, but I just can't accept that kind of thing. She walked out one night recently, left me sitting alone at the table… Mind you, it was a pretty awful place. Said she was feeling sick, and I can't say I could blame her, but it was a terrible thing to happen.'

Cousin Hipwell felt deeply sorry for his friend. 'How did she get home? You don't have a car. She rents a room in the town where she teaches, doesn't she?'

'Simple. She has a car of her own.'

Fred had not told his cousin the whole story.

Edith had turned up at the café extremely smartly dressed. Most of the heads in the dimly lit restaurant turned as the pair came in. Fred pulled out a chair for Edith, but as she sat down, it creaked and swayed. She stood up again as Fred signalled a waiter, and another seat was fetched. In times past, they would have laughed about the situation, but not that evening. The table was covered with cheap oilcloth and when the waiter brought the menu, it was frayed and dog-eared.

Edith chose stew with potatoes and vegetables. When the course was brought, she took a little, then pushed the food around without taking any more. Fred waded through his manfully, but Edith suddenly put the knife and fork down and took a mouthful of water.

'Look, Fred, I can't take any more of this. It's half-heated for a start, and it revolts me.'

Fred looked gloomily over the table, smiling weakly, but Edith was wearing a grim expression. 'I'm sorry, my dear. I just can't afford anything better just now. I've decided to give up at the hospital. I'll ask my father to help me set up a surgery in London. It's not that far away from where you are teaching, and we'll be nearer each other. Once that's up and running, we'll get married. What do you think of that?'

'We've been through all this before, Fred. I've offered to go with you to decent eating places and pay my own, but you won't hear of it…'

Fred flushed with anger. 'You know how I feel about that. If I can't pay the bill, then we don't go out at all. That's it.'

The dim lighting prevented Fred from seeing the danger signs in her face. She spoke sharply. 'How do think I feel, all dressed up to go out with you, and we finish up in a place like this? It reeks of stale food and cigarette smoke. It's not my idea of a night out at all. What's more, you're smoking and drinking again yourself. I can smell it from this side of the table!'

She stood up and drew her wrap around her. 'I think we should call a halt to this.' As she turned to leave, she drew the engagement ring from her finger and laid it on the table in front of Fred, who sat, silent and taken aback, as the door slammed behind her.

A week later, he picked up the telephone in the hall of his rooms and gave the operator her number. Edith answered. She had been longing for the call.

'Fred! I'm so glad to hear from you. How are you?'

They agreed to meet at the weekend, and as two paying lectures had provided enough to eat in a reasonably good café, they enjoyed the food *and* each other's company.

Fred took the little ring box from his pocket and took her hand. 'Is it all right if I put this on again?'

She nodded gently.

For some time, the ring came off and went on again according to the state of affairs between them. Fred's friends and colleagues at the hospital realised that if the ring was dangling from his watch chain, the engagement was off. If it disappeared, it was on again. There were times when Edith was very much in love with him, but when he was abrupt, or angry, she frankly wondered if the next separation should be the last. Weeks could pass without them meeting each other, but when they eventually did, Fred would declare undying passion for her, and she would resolve to keep the relationship going.

Fred came home as autumn 1919 approached. It was to have another talk with his father. They went out to walk around the fields, side by side, William pointing out the various improvements he had made to fencing, roofing or planting sequences. They came to a wooden seat where Margaret and he usually sat when doing their rounds on the Sabbath day.

'Right then, Son, what's on your mind? Have you decided to marry Edith yet?'

'No, father, not yet, but I'm making plans that might help us get there. I can't afford to stay on at the "Sick Chicks". I was sure that they'd offer me a post, but some time ago I'd a row with the physician-in-chief, Alan Brown. He's never liked me and I'm sure he's been blocking my applications for jobs there. Without work that pays enough, I can't marry Edith, but I know she'll not wait for ever. If you're willing to help me, I'd like to take up your offer to lend me enough to buy a place. There's a biggish house I've seen in London that would suit very well. I'll only furnish two rooms – one for consulting patients and the other as a bedroom. I hate having to beg like this, but there's no future for me in Toronto. Surgeons are ten a penny anyway, and the military hospital is coping with the war-wounded pretty well. Even if I finish the course, the qualifications wouldn't bring more work my way. What's more, Edith's teaching at Ingersoll Secondary and, of course, has rooms in the town there. It's only a couple of miles from London, and we can see a lot more of each other that way.'

William did not hesitate. 'Of course I'll help. You should have done this a long time ago. Edith's a fine girl, and I have to say that you've given her a hard time. She's never looked at another man since you left home, while plenty of her friends are married and have kids. I know that's what *she* wants, but you haven't given her much hope. This on-and-off business won't do, and I look to you using this money to get your practice off the ground quickly. Is the house in a good district?'

Fred assured him that he was certain that the bell would never stop ringing once his shingle was on the door. He set off back to Toronto a couple of days later. His resignation from the Sick Children's Hospital was made with some sadness. His friends gave him a cheque, as they knew how hard the financial position was with him.

He used it to buy an old car, and departed for London in it with a cloud of blue smoke following, and a number of alarming noises from the engine.

The town had 60,000 people and was 110 miles west of Toronto.

It was a long journey for such an unreliable car, but after a couple of stops to let the radiator cool down, Fred arrived in London and the next phase in his medical career.

The front door key was difficult to turn at the red-brick house at the corner of Adelaide Street, but Fred managed it eventually. He had some furniture from home, a desk, a few chairs, and some linen inside the car. A few trips downtown to a second-hand furniture store provided a mattress, bed, washstand, a wardrobe, and a card table to eat on, but these were not to arrive until the next day, so he slept on the floor, wrapped in the sheets and blankets from home.

Somewhat sore, he was awake early. Taking the desk and the two chairs, he placed them, first this way, then that, in the room intended for consulting. Finally settling on one chair with its back to the window for himself, the other facing the desk for the patient – or patients, he thought hopefully to himself. The room looked pretty bare, but adequate. The last job was to fix a brass plate on the front doorjamb. It read:

FREDERICK GRANT BANTING, M.D.
SURGEON & GENERAL PRACTITIONER

Taking a cloth from the car, he rinsed it through at the kitchen sink and, making sure there was nobody on the street, gave the plate a final wipe before closing the door.

Edith was a first priority now. Picking up the pedestal telephone on the desk in the surgery, he invited her to come and see the new venture.

'It's what you wanted, Edith, and I'm sure you'll be pleased. Could you come over this weekend? She agreed. 'Come early in the morning. After all, it's not far.'

The ring had been back on her finger for quite some time.

As her car drew up outside and Edith stepped out, the first thing that impressed her was the size of the house. The next was a smiling

Fred waiting on the pavement for her. He kissed and hugged her, took her hand, and led the way inside. As they went through the open door, he pointed proudly at the brass plate, which was shining brightly in the sunshine, partly because it had had yet another polishing just minutes before.

'Come away in. The surgery's in here...'

The limited furnishings were not impressive, but a couple of paintings on the walls brightened the room.

'These are your work, aren't they?' she asked.

'Yes. And when we're married, I'll do more and we'll have them in every room.'

She remembered that some months ago, he had bought a little painting from an art shop for her birthday. It was a simple scene, not particularly skilfully done, but she knew it had been given when he had hardly any income, and treasured it all the more because of that.

'I like painting, Edith, and if I get the chance, I could take lessons later, once I've got going here. You know doctors aren't allowed to advertise, but I'm sure that plate outside'll do the trick, and I can ask you to marry me. This house is big enough to live in – there're three bedrooms – but I'm only using two rooms at the moment. This way to the kitchen; I've got a pot of coffee on the stove.'

The aroma was permeating the atmosphere, giving the place a homely feel. The kitchen was big enough to hold a small table, and crockery was already set out on it.

'Take a seat, Edith.' He poured out the steaming liquid and proffered a plate of biscuits.

She could not help but respond to his enthusiasm over everything. He was like a child with a new toy. They went into town for a light lunch, then a short drive. Stopping at a secluded spot in the country, they spread out a cloth and picnicked in the summer sun. The girl was radiant, full of relief that at last Fred was positive about their future together. Fred had never felt so happy; Edith was certain that wedding bells were not far distant...

As he watched Edith's car draw away after such a romantic time together that weekend, he felt depressed. The brightness that had permeated their talks drained away, and he felt the need of company. He started up the car and went to see Sam Graham, his former roommate from the days in Gloucester Street in Toronto. He too was a doctor, with a practice in Sarnia, another town near London.

The welcome he got was overwhelming. The pair never stopped talking for over an hour – and over the beer that Sam produced from a cupboard at his house. The front doorbell rang, and Fred heard his old friend answer it. Voices could be heard, then Sam came back alone. 'Listen, Fred. That's a patient who's arrived for some surgery, a table-top job – a hernia repair. Must admit I'd forgotten all about him. Why don't you assist, and we'll share the fee fifty-fifty. I work at home here. The surgery's in an annexe along the passage. It'd be much better than taking him to Sarnia Hospital – half the patients pick up infections there and come home with more than they left with – then we can spend the rest of the evening in my favourite hostelry. How about it?' Fred was a skilled anaesthetist and the operation was entirely successful. Once his wound had been stitched and dressed, the patient wanted to go home, so they put him in Sam's car and complied with his request. The fee was twenty dollars, and Fred was more than delighted to have his share. The 'favourite hostelry' turned out to be the local speakeasy, where alcohol was plentiful.

The two men raised their glasses and clinked them together so noisily that the barman glared at them.

'Here's a toast, Fred!' Sam exclaimed. 'Success to us, and you in particular. May your practices all be happy ones!'

The house was bought with a loan of $5500 from his father and $2000 of his own – the last of his savings – and while finance was sufficient for the next few weeks, it was imperative that the practice made money, and quickly at that.

Attracting clients was not easy. While the plate outside was clearly visible to passers-by, there were few passers-by. It was a quiet, residential district. The roads around the houses carried only light traffic, and pedestrians had little need to wander along Adelaide Street.

Day after day, the doctor waited. No footsteps heard outside stopped at the surgery.

Fred had little to do other than write up his diaries, with less and less to set down as the weeks passed. The first full month brought no income whatever; and the next, four dollars. That was for a man needing a prescription for alcohol 'for medicinal purposes'. Prohibition was in force and doctors were authorised to provide these where necessary. August yielded thirty-seven dollars; September, forty-eight.

October's sixty-six came from sporadic anaesthetic, cleft palate and tonsil surgery, and proved that the client level *was* rising, but desperately slowly. Now and then, there were occasional cases that were unusual and successful, such as one that he related to Edith.

'This little fellow was born without a foot. He'd been using a crutch ever since he started to try to walk. To see him so disabled beside his young mother was grim. I took measurements and made a wooden foot with straps that fitted round his calf. To see the look on his face when he stood up and walked around almost normally with it, made my life worthwhile… I've got a job too – demonstrating surgery and anatomy at the Western University a few hours s a week. It's only two dollars an hour, but that's quite a sum to me. It's all helping towards the day you and I can be wed and we can move into this fine big house.'

Soon after, his letters grew more and more depressing.

'The car is costing too much – a breakdown last week cost what was left in my bank. I'll have to sell it and use public transport when we meet in London in future.'

He did not enlarge on his troubles, but by then, his food was heated over the Bunsen burner in the surgery. He was almost at the end of his tether.

November 1920

The subject of a lecture to medical students at the Western University was 'The Pancreas'.

Little was known about this floppy gland situated below and behind the stomach.

Fred had been reading a current month's issue of *Surgery, Gynaecology and Obstetrics*, a leading medical journal. He went to bed with it propped up against his knees, intending to read himself to sleep over it on Sunday night, but sleep did not come. The magazine dropped off the bed as he gave up trying to concentrate on it. His mind was obsessed with finding a way out from the failure of his venture; he was running up more bills every week, bills that were impossible to pay. There was no answer.

To find relief from the torment, he retrieved the magazine and began to read again, marking the sequences he wanted to follow with numbers on the pages.

A section of it caught his eye. It was an article describing a method by which the author had tied off the pancreatic ducts. The pancreas had shrivelled, but cells within it, the 'Islets of Langerhans' had continued to produce a mysterious enzyme, which he had managed to isolate after a fashion. He then injected animals with the serum – animals made diabetic by the removal of their pancreases. The symptoms of diabetes – thirst, constant urination, lethargy and coma – disappeared in most cases, but further researches were stopped when several deaths were attributed to toxicity. Impurities in the extract could not, it seemed, be removed.

As a surgeon, Banting could understand the process clearly. The more he thought about it, the more he felt that more work could produce a means of recovery for the people with diabetes who, at that time, were under sentence of death – and a slow one at that. It was a dreaded diagnosis – there was no cure for a disorder described by physicians centuries earlier. He wrote down in his notebook the following ill-spelled, clumsily written, 'idea' – something that was to be pursued with deep determination over the next period in his life.

DIABETUS

'Ligate pancreatic ducts of dogs. Keep alive until acini degenerate, leaving Islets. Try to isolate the internal secretion of these to relieve glycosuria.'

Students listening to his lecture the following morning noticed that he lacked his normal concentration on the subject, and had to refer to his notes when answering questions at its conclusion. Later in the day, he sought out Professor Miller, head of Physiology at the Western University.

'I've been reading up on the pancreas for the talk I gave this morning and found something I'd like to investigate; it's about diabetes and the effect the pancreas has on converting carbohydrates into energy. If I could speak to someone who is an expert in that field, have the use of a laboratory and some animals… Any chance here?'

Professor Miller stood up from the desk and faced the young man.

'You're not asking for much, are you? Look, we have neither laboratories equipped for that type of work, nor access to animals, but the man you should approach is Professor J.J.R. Macleod at Toronto University.

'He's a well known man in the fields you're referring to, and if you want to mention my name, it might help. He's a very busy man, often abroad, in America, England and here in Canada. Take my advice though: if you *do* get to see him, have all the facts and figures ready. You should set down your objectives and how you're going to achieve them clearly in the letter you send asking for an interview.

'He may seem a bit distant, but he'll be taking in everything you say.'

Rummaging about in his desk, the professor produced several sheets of paper headed 'Western University, St Lewis, Canada'.

'Here. Use these. It might help a bit. Let me know if you are going ahead with the approach, and I'll drop him a note on your behalf.'

Banting had already made up his mind.

'I'd be very grateful if you did, Professor. Doctor Starr's daughter gets married a week on Monday, and I'm invited. Macleod might be able to see me the same day, especially if I write him right now.'

Miller looked somewhat taken aback, but lifted the lid of the desk again and took out another sheet of paper and an envelope.

'Well, I suppose if you are as anxious as that, I'd better do this now.'

CHAPTER 7

1920

The appointment on 27th November with Professor Macleod was for 3.30. Banting did not want to stay overnight as it would use up what little money was in the bank, so he travelled with a day return ticket on the train.

Arriving at the Medical Building a few minutes before the due time, he ran up the stairs to Macleod's office. There was a secretary in an anteroom who, smiling at him, looked up as he entered.

'Doctor Banting... appointment for 3.30...' he said, somewhat breathlessly. The clock on the wall had the hands at exactly that time.

'Yes. Just go in,' she said, indicating a door on her right. 'Can I take your coat?'

He tapped lightly, and a voice invited him to enter.

Professor Macleod – 'JJR' to his friends – was sitting behind a polished, mahogany desk. Standing up, he extended his hand to Banting, who gripped it firmly.

'Doctor Banting? Do have a seat,' he said, indicating an upholstered, leather chair. 'Would you like a coffee? I suggest you try Stella's. It's superb and she keeps it on the brew all the time.' He pressed a buzzer and, almost at once, the secretary put her head round the door.

'Coffee, Professor? I thought you'd want it.' Within a minute, a tray with cups, saucers and biscuits was laid on the desk. She filled the cups and retreated.

'Had you a good trip from London?' Macleod asked. His visitor noticed that the professor had not lost his Aberdeen accent, even although it had been many years since he left Scotland. He was shorter than Banting, who was six feet tall. Macleod was five feet eight.

'Did you come by car?' was the next question.

'No. My car is… off the road. Came by train. Quite a pleasant journey and on time too.'

The professor noted that Banting spoke in an uncultured and countrified accent.

'Well now. I've had a letter from Professor Miller at the Western. He gives you great praise for your demonstrations in surgery and lecturing. I've studied the suggestions you made in yours, but I need more details. Tell me about yourself first. You were in the army during the war – decorated for bravery at the front, I believe?'

Macleod had been doing a little investigation himself into his visitor's records.

His visitor was aware that the professor was studying him with an unwavering gaze, making him hot and ill at ease. It was as if the man was taking in everything that Fred was aware of being wrong about his appearance. The shabby, creased suit was the only one he possessed; his shirt collar overly tight; and his hair unbrushed. His listener was clad in a well-cut, dark suit. The peaks of a snowy-white handkerchief projected from the breast pocket and the pristine shirt cuffs were fastened with gold links. His hair was wavy and neat, as was his bushy moustache. It was obvious to him that Macleod was much older – in fact he was forty-four as opposed to his twenty-eight.

Banting shifted in his seat and, as leather upholstered chairs will, it squeaked loudly.

He began his reply hesitantly. In the presence of strangers, he never felt at ease. He knew that he was about to talk to a man respected throughout Canada, America and Britain for his knowledge in subjects about which Banting knew very little. When writing to ask for an interview, the string of degrees after the professor's name had taken up almost a whole line.

Fred Banting's information about the function of the pancreas and its relationship to the scourge of diabetes had been gleaned within a week of cramming, and during the train journey.

After a slight hesitation in deciding how to open, he began.

'I'd been reading up on the pancreas for a lecture I had to give, and of the way in which a researcher had removed the gland from some animals. They became severely diabetic, showing all the symptoms: lethargy, thirst, constant urination, coma and, soon after, death. It went on to say that by taking the removed pancreases and making up several solutions containing extracts from them, injections were given to the sick animals. Some made a return almost to normality, but many died. The cause was given as toxicity, and the experiments stopped. The writer had been able to prove that the extract had had the effect of reducing the blood sugar, the main cause of death in diabetics. Since the pancreas controls the way that carbohydrates in the diet are converted to energy, there *must* be some way to isolate the mysterious enzyme that brings this about. When the pancreas ceases to produce this chemical, the sufferer becomes ill with diabetes. There is no cure, and thousands die from it. Perhaps by tying off the ducts, it might be possible to persuade the internal cells, the Islets of Langerhans, to exude the secretion and allow the patient to make a recovery. Only by research under laboratory conditions can such answers be found.'

This was the first hint of what the young man had in mind, but it seemed to Banting that the professor was no longer looking at him. He had picked a letter from the tray on the desk, laid it on the blotter in front of him, and appeared to be studying it.

Banting faltered, thinking his listener had lost interest. There was a silence until Macleod looked up.

'Go on then, or is that it?'

'I think, Professor, that I've said as much as I can.'

Macleod seemed again to be engrossed in the page on the desk. Banting began to feel anger rising at this treatment. A trickle of perspiration ran down his forehead. The need for help from Macleod was vital, but he made no comment until quite abruptly, the letter was replaced in the wire tray.

'I have to say, Doctor Banting, that your discussion has been of interest, but I also have to say that it is obvious that you have little experience in the scientific side of what you've proposed. Ever since 1889, when it was discovered that the pancreas held the secret of carbohydrate metabolism, many years of research resulted, and are still ongoing. You have some intriguing theories in your "idea", but have you not heard of the German, Zuelzer or Paulescu, the Romanian? It's likely that Germany would have produced a successful treatment by now, but the country was bankrupted by the war. Medical research was the last thing on the agenda; but Paulescu, now there's a man who *is* nearing a solution. He's been working on pancreatic extracts for years.

'You must realise that success will not simply fall into your lap. It'll mean long days and nights of work. It's not like surgery, where your patient makes a recovery, dies, or lives on, disabled in some way.

'You say you want the use of our facilities here in Toronto. Well, it's true we have the finest equipment in Canada, but it isn't available right now. Write me again next spring, will you? I'll make arrangements with you then. Even if your "idea" doesn't work, it'll be of great physiological interest.'

Macleod was patently concluding the interview. Shaking hands again, Banting turned towards the door. He was confused and unhappy.

The professor's apparent loss of interest was a habit that had infuriated a fair number of others, but he had been listening closely all the time.

Stalking past the girl in the outer office without giving her a glance, Banting was outside in the corridor when he remembered his coat. Turning, he was part-way back, when Stella met him, carrying it. Mumbling an apology, he resumed the fast walking until outside in the street. He was till hot and sweaty, but the November air cooled him quickly.

In the train, he went over what the professor had said. He knew his own performance had been poor. The business with his interviewer appearing to lose interest in what he was trying so hard to explain was still rankling. The elegance of Macleod's office had also slightly overawed Fred: the hatstand with the bowler hat and umbrella hanging there, quality pictures and framed certificates on the walls, and, most of all, the smartness of the professor himself. It was easier now, calmed by the changing scenery outside the carriage window, to reassess what had passed between them.

Gradually, the final comments from Macleod registered. The obsessive need to persuade the other to give his support had knocked Fred Banting off the track. The final part of the interview was just a blur, but now more relaxed, he realised that his request *had* indeed been granted. The delay was unavoidable – the professor had said something about the Christmas break and staff not being available for a few months…

Banting began to construct a pattern of how the research might begin. The others in the carriage noticed that he had fallen asleep.

Back in London, he telephoned Edith. He spoke excitedly.

'I'm on the way! I'm gonna get the use of the labs at the university, animals, everything! If I can succeed with this work, I'll be famous – and rich too! My "idea" *will* work, I'm sure of it. But I can't go to Toronto until the spring, and that's a long time.'

There was silence from the other end of the line.

'Edith darling, are you there?'

A few seconds elapsed and when she spoke, the strain in her voice was plain.

'Yes, Fred. I'm so glad the trip was worthwhile. You got on all right with the professor then?'

'To be honest, I had a rough passage. I can't say I like him, but he was OK, I suppose... He's so distant, and I felt like a country hick in my shabby clothes and grubby shoes. Pity Kells wasn't still around. He used to shine my boots until I could see myself in them. Still, Macleod agreed to co-operate, and that's the main thing.'

Edith was only part listening. She foresaw that whatever happened in Toronto, it was going to take a while. Marriage would be out of the question until her fiancé could earn enough money. Would he get any salary during his investigations, she wondered?

Fred had never said anything about that, nor had Macleod. She refrained from mentioning this; it was not the time.

The plate outside London's Adelaide Street surgery no longer shone in the sun's rays. It was not because Fred Banting was so busy that time did not allow for this; it was because worry over finance was constantly present. Although the confidence that the venture would succeed had not gone and more patients *were* turning up, the payments were not nearly enough to cover food, clothing, the loan and all the other outlays that are encountered in owning a house. When taking Edith out however, he did without things to save up enough to dine out at better-quality places.

1921

The winter passed all too slowly for Fred. His lectures continued to bring in a little extra cash, but instead of studying literature on diabetes and the pancreas, he spent time with Professor Miller at the Western University, where their work had nothing to do with these topics. It was almost as if he had detached himself from the whole 'idea' that had fired him up in the autumn.

He heard nothing from Toronto University until a letter arrived in February, inviting him to 'further discussions' with the professor in early March. This prompted a flurry of activity into studies of the now prioritised subjects.

This time, the professor was much warmer than on the last call.

* * *

'I've been thinking about your "idea", Doctor Banting. Your suggestion is not new – the tying off of ducts to the pancreas has already been done within the last thirty years of research, with mixed results. The thing is, you are a surgeon, something none of the others were, and therein lies the strength of your proposals. Your techniques may well have an influence on the isolation of this long-sought serum. You are, however, more likely to succeed with the assistance of another, and I have in mind two young graduates, both brilliant but not yet qualified, one of whom will join you to do the laboratory work, keep records and so on.'

Banting frowned at this. He did not want an assistant, but had no option other than to let Macleod finish. The buzzer was depressed, and the secretary came in.

'Miss Clutton, would you ask Noble and Best to come in, please; and bring a pot of your delectable coffee too.'

Two tall men appeared, and Banting stood up to shake hands with them. They were carrying extra chairs, and sat themselves down as Stella reappeared with the customary tray. It was the first time Banting had learned that her surname was Clutton.

Macleod then sprang another surprise. 'My budget won't stretch to two assistants, Doctor Banting. They are both fourth-year students in Physiology and Biochemistry – ideal to help and keep records of your researches. I suggest this be decided by the throw of a coin. I've a fifty-cent piece here. Perhaps Stella would do the job?'

Stella had been filling the cups with steaming coffee and looked surprised, but took the coin and held it ready.

'Right, Stella. Heads it's Best; tails it's Noble. Throw!'

She spun it, caught it in her right hand, transferred it to the back of her left, and held it out so that everyone could see it. They craned forward as Macleod looked at the shiny coin.

'Heads! You have the post, Best. You can look forward to an interesting time with Doctor Banting, and I wish you both the best of good fortune. I thank you for attending, Mister Noble. There may be work you can do later to further this investigation.' Clark Noble left the room quietly.

'I'll see you all later,' was all he said.

'I'll leave the two of you to decide when you want to start. May should see the labs ready for you, and I'll arrange a supply of dogs for your work.' Macleod's words concluded the meeting.

Near Banting's surgery in London was another, run by a young doctor, Bill Tew. The two had become good friends. They met for a drink after Fred's meeting in Toronto.

'Well then, Fred, how'd things go?' Tew asked. He knew how mixed his colleague's feelings had been after the first session with the professor.

'I'm not very happy about this one either, Bill. The professor wants me to have an assistant – more or less forced me to take this young whippersnapper who's hardly dry behind the ears. He's studying science and physiology, and the proff says he's bright. We'll see. His name's Charles Best and he's also an ex-army man – cavalry, I think. Likes horses, anyway. Seems pretty well off judging by the cut of his jib. Mind you, he's a likeable lad. Suppose I'll just need to put up with him, whatever he's like.'

Tew lifted his glass.

'Here's to success, Fred. Don't get upset over young Best. If you succeed with your research and it leads to a treatment that'll stop people dying, you'll have the world at your feet, and you can tell the professor where to get off…

'What're you going to do about the surgery? You can hardly

keep that on when you'll be in Toronto most of the time.'

Ordering another couple of pints of beer, Fred lit a cigarette.

'Don't know. I had hoped that by now, Edith and I would have been married and living at Adelaide Street,' he said, wistfully.

'I must say, I'm surprised that a good-looking girl has waited so long, Fred,' Tew commented. 'I'm sure my wife wouldn't have waited more than three years like Edith has.'

Fred lit another cigarette. 'Can't imagine why, either, Bill. After all, we got engaged in 1918, it'll be spring this year before I can even start the research, and goodness knows how long that'll take. Yes, I'm lucky to have Edith putting up with me so long, but there it is. I *must* get on with this research though, so whatever time it takes, it takes. Things have changed between us too; we've both matured a lot. She wants marriage. I want that too, but can't – you understand why, Bill – so it's an impasse.'

Bill Tew looked at his friend as he stood up to leave. Fred was pale, stooped and gaunt, and had obviously lost weight. Tew could not do other than feel sorry for him. He was going home to a warm, happy family. Fred's return was to a cold, cheerless and empty house – not much of a life.

Bill Tew dropped Fred off at Adelaide Street. Opening the front door to a chilled hallway, he trudged through to his bedroom. Washing his face at the bathroom sink, the water was stone cold. There was no heating of any kind in the house, so he fetched out an old electric fire and plugged it in. The smell of the burning dust on the element rose in the air, but the single bar soon gave out a cheering heat.

'T'hell with the cost of running this,' he mumbled to himself. Only the warming red of the fire lit the room. Sitting on the edge of the bed, he tried to decide what to do about the house, about Edith, about the future. Coming to no conclusion about any, he slipped his tie and shoes off and turned in to bed. It was too cold to undress.

In the few weeks left before leaving for Toronto, there were matters to tidy up at the university. There was a lecture to give to a fourth-year class, an examination to supervise, reports to write up, and the balance of fees to collect.

On the last day, a delegation of students appeared with a box of good quality cigars.

'We're going to miss you, Sir. The best of luck, and these are for you.'

He left with a warm glow in his heart. It was good to know the students had thought so much of him.

CHAPTER 8

May 1921

The weight of two bulging suitcases made hard going of Fred Banting's progress up to the entrance to cousin Hipwell's house in Toronto. Lugging them to the front door, he got a surprise when it flew open and Lillian, Frederick Hipwell's wife, welcomed him by taking one from his hand. She had seen him coming and shouted to her husband, 'Frederick! Come here! It's Fred! Hurry up! How far have you carried these? This one weighs a ton. Come away in, Fred. Husband obviously hasn't heard. Leave that other case in the hall here. We'll sort it all out later. Did you have a good trip from London? You must be hungry. C'mon through to the kitchen, 'cos that's where your cousin's washing the dishes.'

Fred Banting had not been able to utter a word, but he knew Lillian's welcomes were never less than boisterous. He was always made to feel at home in this place where his old school and drug-store habitué had bought a house.

The upshot of the one-sided conversation was an invitation to eat right away and later, to stay with them. At the dinner table, the conversation was all about Fred's starting the research and its programme.

'When do you take up this work?' Hipwell asked, during a lull in his wife's chatter.

'The seventeenth,' Fred answered.

'That's tomorrow!' Hipwell exclaimed.

'Yes. That's right!' Fred replied.

'Better get upstairs and have an early night's shut-eye then…'

Stella Clutton was just lifting the big coffee pot from the electric heating ring she kept for the purpose in a corner when Banting arrived. The tray with crockery and biscuit plate was ready, so she led the way. Fred came behind, carrying the coffee pot, and found Charles Best already sitting in the office. He stood up and shook hands as Banting took the other chair in front of the big desk. After the cups were filled, Macleod took a pipe, packed it with tobacco, and put a match to it.

'Right now,' he opened, 'I have a lot of work to do this morning, so I suggest that Best takes you up to the labs. I've given orders that they be cleaned and made ready. I hope they're all right as I haven't had time to look at them myself. There are some animals in the room next door, and there should be a desk for writing up records and reports. Once you've settled in up there – it's on the top floor – go and have lunch in the dining room. Put it on my bill.'

Lifting a folder, he handed it to Banting.

'These are a few notes with some guidelines for you. There is a detailed section on the new method of doing blood sugar tests – a very important way of checking the effectiveness of any treatment you devise. Keep a careful record of these results. The research is, after all, in my name, so I hope that you'll make a point of keeping me advised on progress. We could meet fairly often – perhaps lunch together, which will save some of your time since you could give me your reports verbally. I'll come up at 2.00 p.m. tomorrow. If you care to have the surgery for a pancreas excision prepared, I'll observe, if that's all right with you, gentlemen? Good luck.'

Without waiting for further comment, he drank the last of his coffee, stood up, and went to the door, taking his cup and saucer back to Stella. He did not come back, but carried on along the passage. Somewhat overwhelmed, Banting and Best followed suit. They had expected a somewhat more leisurely beginning.

'D'you know where this suite is?' Fred asked Best.

'Yes. I have two sets of keys too. Here's a set for you. I'll keep the other, in case we're working overtime. Call me Charley, by the way. Everybody knows me as Charley,' the young man said.

'You already know my name is Frederick; Fred'll do,' Banting replied.

They climbed the stairs to the top floor, walked along a corridor, and came to a door which Charley opened with the key. It was difficult to turn, and the bottom of the door scraped along the floor with a grating sound. Inside, the scene might have been straight from a horror film set. Dust covered everything. The benches were lined with dusty retorts and glass containers, some with dark, coloured liquids left in them after some long-completed experiment. There was a desk in a corner, but papers had fallen out of the inner recesses and lay on the filthy floor.

'Well, well!' Charley remarked to a silent Banting. 'I'm afraid that whoever got the orders from JJR to clean the place hasn't been here.'

There was a bark from the room next door. 'At least the dogs are,' Fred muttered.

They found them in a large room adjacent to the laboratory. The wire cages were clean, with ample sawdust on the floors and bowls of fresh water in each. The animals stood up on hind legs, pushing their noses through the mesh excitedly.

'This is a bit better,' Fred observed. 'But the rest of the place is a mess. Look, Charley, I want to get started quickly. Are you willing to give this place a good doing? By the time we find who should have done this, it'll take hours. There's plenty hot water in the taps there. Would you see if you can scrounge around and get scouring powder? I'll see if I can find brushes and cloths.'

Charley disappeared, and Fred opened a cupboard. He found not only brushes and mops, but buckets, scouring powder and floor cloths.

A set of stairs led upward. There was a top housing which gave onto the flat roof. It looked vast. The only interruptions were chimney stacks and ventilators. A parapet encircled the outer edges. Charley had reappeared down below by the time Fred had inspected the roof area, had a cigarette and decided that the rooftop would be ideal for exercising the dogs.

The buckets were filled with steaming water, sloshed over the wooden floors, and the two began to mop the mess into a thick slurry. This was lifted with the cloths and wrung out over the sinks. They had begun on their knees with scrubbing brushes when there was a sudden, thunderous hammering at the door. Opening it, a red-faced young man was standing there.

'What the hell do you think you're doing? We're on the floor beneath and there's filthy water dripping down on us. You'll have to stop that.' He was obviously furious, and perhaps justifiably so. His suit was covered with dark stains. He turned on his heel before either of the men could say a word, his heels clicking angrily away down the corridor.

Fred and Charley exchanged looks. Charley began to smile and within a couple of seconds, the pair, unable to move because of their hysterical laughter, eventually sobered up.

'We'd better finish cleaning this up, get rid of all this water slopping around. Once that's away, it'll not be so bad...' Fred remarked. They worked until well after midnight, cleaning not only the floors, but all the containers on the benches as well as the desk and cupboards.

At last, exhausted, they finished.

'How early can you be here tomorrow morning?' Fred asked.

Fred arrived soon after the dawn began to colour the buildings of Toronto, but he was not interested in the view. The first item was something on which to perform surgery. There were only some cleaners in the building at that time if day but, finding a woman polishing the floor in a passage, he explained what he wanted. Stopping her work, she leant on the handle of the polisher. She told him at once where he might get one.

'The janitor got a table that had a castor off. He was gonna put it out. He's in an office at the entrance.'

Fred came back upstairs with a table that was just right: the right height, the right area, and, by taking the other three castors off, good and steady.

He also obtained a rubberised sheet to put over it, and by arranging an electric lamp immediately above, stood back to admire his handiwork just as Charley opened the door.

'Hey! Not bad at all,' he enthused. 'I've brought some towels along to lay the animals on while you're doing your stuff.'

Fred nodded his approval and lit a cigarette. 'Need to get an ashtray,' he remarked. 'I think we'd better be ready for JJR – he'll probably be bang on time.'

Charley hung his jacket up and slipped on a newly laundered lab coat. It was dazzling in its whiteness. He prepared for action, making an anaesthetising mask ready and laying out instruments at the end of the table. When the professor walked in at the stroke of two, he was, as before, immaculately dressed. Charley handed him a clean towel to use as an apron, but it was waved away.

'I'm just here to see how things go. You've been busy, I see.' Neither said that the promise that the place would be ready for them had not been kept. They had had no lunch.

Fred lifted a dog, a big Alsatian cross, out of its cage, stood it on the table, and Best held it by the legs while the surgeon put the animal to sleep. When it lay sprawled on the table, Charley handed the instruments to his superior.

Macleod kept up a running commentary as Banting worked.

'You're going to cut out most of the pancreas, bring part of it forward, and stitch it in place just under the skin, having severed and tied off the ducts surrounding it?'

'Yes.'

You are hoping that this process will cause the pancreas to wither and exude its inner fluid?'

'Yes.'

'Finally, the remaining piece of pancreas still in the original position will keep the animal alive until it is finally removed, and the extract from the retained piece is used to treat other severely diabetic dogs?'

Banting could only nod, as it was essential to concentrate on the bleeding animal in front of him. Standing back for a moment, he wiped his forehead with his sleeve. He was perspiring heavily.

The operation was complex. The pancreas in a human being is difficult to access, behind the stomach. In an animal, it is so much smaller and almost jelly-like, and it was the first time Banting had attempted removal of one in such a manner. Perhaps if the professor's guidelines had been read, the process might have been easier, but the folder lay unopened. In view of the first flush of enthusiasm, they could perhaps hardly be blamed.

The sweat on Banting's face was running down and dripping off his chin. The room was already hot, and, as the day progressed, it got even warmer – the forerunner of a record heatwave in Toronto.

The professor fell suddenly silent, his gaze on the animal on the table and the difficulty of the job that the surgeon was carrying out was expressionless. Suddenly Macleod turned away. 'All right. I've got to leave you, gentlemen.'

They heard the outer door rasp on the floor as he left. The atmosphere became relaxed without his presence as the two men exchanged looks.

'What do you make of that?' Fred remarked. 'Is he interested or not?'

Charley said nothing. He could see for himself that Fred was struggling. Most surgeons he had watched had been deft and confident. Fred was not having an easy time, pulling parts of the dog's digestive system out of the way in a welter of blood.

Finally, the stitching was finished and Fred went to wash his hands. Charley took swabs to clear blood away from the operation site. He too cleaned up at the sink, then returned to the surgery room

'Number One's coming round, Fred.' The young assistant had noticed the dog stirring slightly.

Fred came over. 'Leave it there just now. Put some wadding in its cage to make it more comfortable. Take a blood test in an hour, and every hour after. That'll let us keep a record of what's happening to its sugar levels.'

'Will we see something of this "mysterious secretion" by tomorrow?' Charley enquired.

'Maybe, but I suspect it may take much longer than that. My own "idea" is that the pancreas has to degenerate for about seven weeks before it will exude what we're looking for.'

Actually, he had no idea how long it would take, or even if it would happen at all.

What took place over the next few days did not augur well.

Charley was giving an anaesthetic to another animal. Fred was writing a report when he heard Charley call him.

'Fred! Come here. Quickly!' Taking the mask away from the dog's face, he lifted the beast and shook it gently. 'It's not breathing.'

The surgeon held his hand over the heart. 'It's not likely to, Charley. It's dead. You've given it too much chloroform.'

During the next attempt, the dog haemorrhaged while Fred was operating. He was unable to stem the flow of blood, and the animal died half an hour later. Finally, the original dog died of an infection before the two worried researchers learned the proper technique that stopped the repeated disasters taking place during their initial attempts.

The faithfully entered diary read:

'This has been a terrible week. So many animals died. Charley and I may have been careless; we are certainly not callous. Hope that the next trials may work better.'

27 May

The last words in Fred Banting's diary had been wishful thinking.

Still keeping to his dawn arrival at the laboratory, he sat at the desk thinking, trying to see what alternative way there was to further his 'idea'. Each entry in the journal showed few changes; the only changes were in the number of days the subjects took to die, some within hours. The rooms reeked of cigarette smoke as they were often lit from the stub of the last. As the heatwave got underway, the smell of the dogs was also so pervasive that the two men were forced to clean out the cages and wash the floors more often to keep the stench down.

The sun was up one day when Charley sauntered in, his sports jacket draped over one shoulder, his silk shirt open at the neck. He gave a brief 'Good morning' to Banting, then started to don his lab coat. He was supposed to go, first thing, to feed the animals, get the bowls filled with fresh water, see to those recovering (or otherwise), and report to Fred if necessary.

Instead, he came over to the desk.

'Sorry to interrupt, but can I get off for about ten days? There's a military exercise on, and you know I was a sergeant in the Artillery. I need to let my commanding officer know.'

He could not have asked this at a worse time.

Fred slammed the thick book shut with a bang so loud that Charley stepped back a pace.

'D'you mean to tell me that less than a week after starting, you want to disappear for *that* length of time? We're in deep trouble and I need you here. It's all right for you, but I think this is a bit much. Go and attend to the dogs and I'll think about it.' He turned back to the book and opened it again.

Charley took his time. In one cage, a dog lay inert while the others were barking and scraping at the wire.

He carefully lifted the animal out and laid it on the towel-covered table. Taking his stethoscope, he listened to the heart. Straightening up, he went through to the lab. Fred was still poring over the record book.

'Fred, I'm sorry, but there's another animal very poorly. The heart's irregular and it's unconscious. It's the one that had surgery on Friday. I looked in on Saturday and Sunday to feed them, and all the dogs seemed OK then. Could you come and have a look?'

Wearily, Fred trudged through to the room. By the time he reached the operating table, the dog was dead. He looked over to his sad-eyed assistant. His temper had calmed and he had decided to let the young man go to his exercise.

'Come up on the roof, Charley. The air's cooler up there, and we'll talk about this.'

Making their way over to the ledge, they sat down. Charley got a cigarette going and looked out over the wooded street below.

'We've only got four dogs left out of the ten that JJR allocated to us. He's away to Washington at a conference, so we could do something about the situation while he's away. He hasn't seen any reports yet, and won't do for another week or two. There's a way out of this. There are plenty of strays roaming the streets in Toronto. We could round up a few and get on with the work.

Charley nodded slowly. 'We could give the same number to the replacements in the logbook as the ones that have died, I guess. We could maybe buy some if we can't catch any. There're always some available when people get tired of them. Let's go out tonight and see if we can pick up any. They'd be better cared for here than they'd ever be out there…'

It was on Charley's conscience that while care of them would be better than out on the streets, the same could not be said of their life expectancy…

There was no difficulty in finding stray dogs that night. Fred came back with three, and Charley bought one for two dollars from an alcoholic in a speakeasy.

By the next night, the number was back to the original total.

Charley waited until the middle of the week before daring to raise the question of his military sojourn.

'Fred, I need to let my commander know about attendance at the exercise. I know how hard it'll be for you to do without me for over a week, but…'

Fred swivelled round to face him. 'Yes… I'd forgotten about that. Well, I guess you can. You know I was in the Army too, at the front in the last few weeks of the war. There was certainly plenty of action. That's where I got wounded – in this arm. The only good thing about it is the small pension I get. It's about the only money I have coming in just now.'

Charley knew a little about the episode.

'That's how you were decorated – for bravery wasn't it?' Charley noted the admiration in the young man's face.

'Well yes. They called it "pluck" actually, but I suppose it's the same thing.'

'I'd like to see the medal some day.'

Fred never brought it in and forgot all about Charley's request. There were more important things to think about.

Soon after Charley left, there was a request from Stella Clutton to come and make an appointment with the professor after his return. He went down to her office at once.

'Hi there, Fred,' she greeted the tired looking man. 'How're you doing? Sit down over there a minute, if you've time.'

'I have to say, not very well, Stella. The plan isn't working yet, but we'll get there eventually. The heat is the worst thing. It's just a tarred and felted roof above us and, between the stink from the dogs and the temperature, it's not ideal for what we're doing.'

He eyed the big fan that was whirring away on the windowsill. He explained that because of Best's absence, cleaning and care of the dogs was being done by himself.

Stella did not need all the details about the conditions under which the men were working. She could smell Fred from where she was sitting a couple of yards away, particularly when he leant over her desk to open his diary. They fixed a date a couple of weeks ahead, and he returned to the chair once it was pencilled in.

'Look, Fred, you should take the chance to tell the professor about the surroundings you're working in. It just won't have occurred to him – he's a tremendously busy man, you know. You need to be quick, because he and his wife go back to Scotland every year from June until September.

It was a surprise to Banting that the head of the department would be absent for so long, but the university more or less closed down during much of the summer and the students went home or took jobs for the period.

'And another thing…' Stella put down the paper she had been typing and turned to face Fred. 'Can you not take an iron to that suit? You were wearing it the first time you came here last year. You mustn't let JJR see you like that! Are you putting some kind of detergent on the floor when you scrub them. You smell of that as well as the animals! All that plus cigarettes is pretty overwhelming, I can tell you. Forgive me, Fred, but I had to tell you.'

Fred flushed angrily. Reaching into his pocket, he brought out a few coins – seven cents – and slammed them on Stella's desk.

'What you see there is all the money I have. The suit I'm wearing is the only one I possess, and only money will buy another. There's no pay for all this bloody work I'm doing. Young Best gets a salary because he's a student. He's classified as a researcher. I don't get anything except a few dollars for assisting the surgeons over at the hospital next door, and that's only now and then. How can I keep myself looking decent on that?' He began to pick up the coins.

Stella felt deeply sorry for the man sitting in the corner. He looked so thin and white. His situation was totally unknown to her up to then, and she had nothing to do with forms of employment at the university. She would have liked to help, but it was absolutely improper for a person in her position to interfere in any way. She put a cup of coffee on the desk and poured one for herself.

'Look, I've had an idea. Bring the suit in here to me tomorrow. I'll have it cleaned and pressed over at the hospital laundry. They'll do it for me if I ask, and it'll be back the day after. You can surely borrow something to wear for your visit to JJR. Anything would be better than what you've got on! Now don't object. Leave it to me.'

Fred's pride was going to get in the way again, but she managed to persuade the reluctant Banting to accept.

'Well... all right. It's very good of you to care so much.' He trudged off, shoulders hunched, figure bent, wondering what he could wear once the offending suit and he parted company.

A few days later, Banting appeared back at Stella's office. She welcomed him with her customary cheerfulness.

'My, Fred! How much smarter you look today.' He had cousin Hipwell's Sunday rigout on – a double-breasted, good quality suit. It was a good fit.

'I'm not cleaning out the lab today, so's my cousin gets it back with no bad smells attached to it,' he told her, grinning.

'And here's yours back,' she said, holding out a brown paper parcel to him. 'See and look after it. Now, your appointment with the professor is this afternoon. I'll see you then.'

Banting returned at the appointed time. Stella led him into where Macleod was seated at his desk writing some notes.

'Come away, Doctor. Good to see you. Take a seat until I finish this.'

Stella appeared with her tray; Banting offered to pour out. Once the cups were full, Macleod set the work aside and sat back, filling and lighting his pipe.

'That's that. Now, how are things going?'

'Frankly, I haven't much to tell you, Professor. It is, after all, early days. We have removed pancreases successfully, but until the period of time I estimated in my theory – seven weeks – we cannot make extracts with which to treat the diabetic dogs. Here's our record book, but all it shows is the mounting blood sugars after the pancreatic ducts were tied off.'

Macleod laid the book down and took a pen to run own the columns.

'I see what you mean, Doctor, but that is only to be expected. The first surgery was performed the day I left for Washington – the seventeenth of last month. This is the third of June, so you've a wee while to wait, have you not?' The stiff-covered register was handed back with a smile.

The meeting had gone well, although Banting did not tell his listener that some of the numbers logged in the book actually applied to two animals – one deceased and one alive.

He consoled himself by reasoning that the results would have been the same in any case.

Macleod came to the door with him.

'One other thing. My wife and I leave for Scotland later this month. Her parents and my relatives live there, and we'll return in September, in time for the university opening again in October. I'd like you to write me frequently to keep me in the picture.'

Banting nodded.

The professor continued.

'I've made some further notes for you that might help your project along a bit. Let Best have a read of them too. If anything spectacular happens, you can send me a telegram, even phone me as the transatlantic cable works very well. I've been able to speak to colleagues and relatives that way. You'll excuse me now: there's a lot to do before we leave.'

Banting stood as Macleod put his hand out with a comment, 'Good luck with this work. If it succeeds, the two of you will have brought great honour to Canada and in particular to Toronto University.' The professor turned back as Banting left. He suddenly realised that he had not touched Stella's coffee, but she appeared just then with the tray carrying Macleod's empty cup and Banting's full one. She poured out another and insisted he finish it.

The heatwave in summer was already at record levels. It was difficult for Fred Banting to develop his 'idea' without assistance from young Best. Although he would never have admitted it, he missed his company too. An unexpected late payment from the Western University made him decide to take a break and go home to the farm for a few days, leaving a few dollars with a porter to look after the animals.

Edith and he had not been able to meet for some time. The only contact was a weekly phone call. Arriving at Alliston station, his father was waiting for him with the pony and trap.

Molly was between the shafts, and 'spoke' to him with her usual short whinnies. He fed her a couple of sugarlumps and she scrunched them noisily. At the farmhouse, William dismounted and tied the pony up at the rail.

'Put your bag in the house, Fred. You'll be wanting to see Edith, so I'll leave Molly here and you can use the trap once you've cleaned up.'

Before Fred set off, he telephoned Edith. She answered very promptly.

'Fred! You're home then. Your father told me at church on Sunday you were thinking about coming this weekend. How long are you staying? Are you coming over?'

Assuring her he was about to set off, minutes later he climbed up onto the seat of the trap. He took his time on the short journey in order to think what he might say to his fiancée. What *could* he say? She would be upset when he told her about the slow progress at the university.

Edith's parents insisted on tea and biscuits, but knew that the young couple would want to be alone together, and excused themselves as soon as propriety allowed.

Edith put her arms around Fred and kissed him.

'You've lost a lot of weight, Fred! I can feel your bones through your clothes. Are the Hipwells feeding you well enough? Oh, Fred! It seems so long since we met.'

It was true that he was thinner. It was not lack of food that was the cause; it was anxiety.

The house in London was still empty and unsold. Worry about the success or failure of the project in Toronto, worry about lack of enough cash to pay his way, and worry about the situation between Edith and himself were seemingly insurmountable problems.

'Come and sit over here beside me,' Edith invited, patting the settee cushion beside her. 'Tell me how the work is going. Are you making much headway?'

Taking her hands, Fred drew her away a little, but it did not stop Edith from carrying on with an outpouring of words.

'It's so frustrating. All the girls I knew when I was at school are married. Most have kids already, or boyfriends who take them out dancing or drinking. I'm stuck with my parents at weekends. I can't go out with anyone. That'd be frowned on when I'm engaged. I'd be talked about. Yet I earn a good salary. I just put the money in the bank, where all it does is earn interest. It's no good the way things are, Fred. I'd like to have babies too, but if things drag on much longer I'll be too old.'

The torrent slackened as emotion overcame her. Fred took her in his arms to console her when he saw tears well in her eyes. It was all getting too emotional for him.

'My darling Edith. Just a little longer and I'll be able to wed. Just a little longer. You know how much I love you, need you. Everything *you* want, I want. We're definitely on the right track. The professor told me that just a few days ago, but I had to take a break.

'When success comes, I'll be wealthy beyond my wildest

dreams. You can have a beautiful house with everything in it you want. Lots of room for the babies, all the gadgets in the kitchen, a car for yourself, money in the bank. I just need time.'

Edith had recovered and spoke quietly but firmly.

'I'd be perfectly happy in a two-roomed shack as long as I was with you, Fred. The picture you paint is lovely, but I don't need all that. After all, I'm just an ordinary girl who's been engaged for more than three years, but no wedding yet. Why can't you realise that? You look worn out, dearest. All this terrible strain you're going through. Could you not give all this up and go back to London? The practice was beginning to pick up, and you've still got the house.'

It was, as Fred remarked later to cousin Hipwell, an impasse. Neither could accept the other's viewpoint, and Edith was becoming desperate.

Banting returned from Alliston, his mental state in tatters. Nothing was going well, but he determined to start work again and, as urged by the professor, take more frequent blood sugar tests. When he went to the benches to look out the equipment, he found the glassware dirty, the test tubes unclean. They had obviously been neglected for some time.

He washed out enough to carry out the experiments, and left the rest. Charley was due back the next day, so he nursed his anger, saving it up for a showdown.

As it happened, Charley appeared that evening, a grin on his tanned face.

'Hi there, Fred,' he opened. 'How did you manage without me?'

The greeting was the blue touchpaper that caused the explosion that followed.

'How dare you come in here like that!' was Fred's opening salvo. 'Just look at the state this glassware's in. Our work can't possibly succeed when the equipment is filthy. According to Macleod, you're a blue-eyed boy. Not in my book!'

Charley blushed deep red; the attack was the last thing he had expected. Anger ran through him like a storm as he struggled to keep control. After an eyeball to eyeball confrontation, he had to turn away and mumble an apology. His senior returned to the desk and opened the record book.

Charley set to at once, filling the sinks with hot, soapy water and, beginning at one end of the benches, rinsed out every single item on the shelves. Fred took off his lab coat and muttered an almost inaudible good night as he left. Charley was still working, sleeves rolled up, at the sink.

When they arrived within minutes of each other next morning, nothing more was said, but Fred could hardly miss the rows of gleaming equipment lining every bench and shelf.

CHAPTER 9

June 1921

It was on one of the hottest days that summer that Fred met cousin Hipwell and his wife. They had not seen him for a few weeks as he had moved out from their house and was in rooms of his own near the university. Lillian, pushing a pram, saw him first from the other side of the street.

'Fred! Fred!' she called. 'Over here. Come over here!' He was back to his stooped way of walking. It was obvious that he was deeply engrossed in thought and would not have seen them had she not shouted a greeting. He came over the road and gave Lillian a hug.

'You look terrible,' she announced. 'You aren't feeding yourself properly since you left us, are you?'

'I was on the way to get something,' he mumbled, not telling her that his destination was the Philatea Club at the church, where meals were still almost as cheap as before the war.

'Well look, it's Friday and we usually go out in the car for a picnic with the baby at the weekend. We'll pick you up tomorrow and you can come with us.'

Fred shook his head, but before he could speak, Lillian carried on at her usual breakneck speed.

'You can tell me where you'd like us to take you. We often find a place on the beach on Lake Ontario. Right, then. Half past ten tomorrow. Be ready now.'

Her husband raised an eyebrow and smiled at Fred.

'Just do as you're told,' he said, taking his wife's arm. The couple walked away, leaving Fred alone on the sidewalk.

The car pulled up outside Fred's rooms at the time suggested. Lillian Hipwell had the baby on her knee on the front seat. Fred pushed a travelling rug and a big wicker picnic basket out of the way, and clambered into the back. An hour later they stopped at a quiet stretch of sand lapped by the waters of the lake. Frederick and his wife unpacked cups, plates, sandwiches and biscuits from the basket as Fred took the rug and spread it out. All three settled themselves comfortably while Lillian propped the infant up on cushions. They could feel the warmth of the sand through the rug.

'Now then, Fred,' Lillian started, 'just you tuck into this food. Do you want some lemonade? I made it myself. And there's some of my fresh baking in that tin. Help yourself.'

Soon after, her husband set off for a walk along the shore. Fred went with him, leaving Lillian with the baby. The men went side by side along the water's edge without speaking for some minutes, then cousin Hipwell opened. 'You're very quiet, Fred. Things not going well?'

'I have to say we've had some problems. But they'll resolve themselves. The trouble is that the animals are dying from infections caused by the heat. It's not easy to get at the pancreas in small animals, and some are *very* small, I can tell you.'

Frederick, also being a doctor, could understand the problem. 'Yes. It must make such complicated surgery very difficult. Do you have to deal with the pancreas the way you're doing? Why keep it stitched under the animal's skin? If you sutured it somewhere externally, you could observe it more easily, see when the outer layer has degenerated, try isolating the Islets of Langerhans quicker than waiting seven weeks?'

Fred walked more slowly. He was thinking. 'You might have something there. It'd be worth a try anyway.'

When they returned to the picnic spot, the baby was fast asleep and Lillian was dozing. She sat up and tended the child. 'You'd be as well with another sandwich before we leave, Fred. And there's some lemonade left in the bottle.'

Fred shook his head. 'Thanks, Lillian. If I eat any more, I'll not be able to get up, but I'll have another glass of your lemonade, thanks.' He sat, legs outstretched and relaxed, the furrows on his brow less deeply etched, swaying liquid back and forth in the bottom of the glass before draining it.

'This has been a great time for me today,' he said, putting the empty glass with the others in the basket, and making the baby chuckle as he tickled it with his finger.

'I feel so much better and more able to think straight. I must have sounded a bit down when I was telling you about the problems at the lab, Frederick, but I've decided to press on. My "idea" *will* work. Between Charley and I, we'll make it. We were beginning to think we'd have to give up, but we won't win unless we keep trying. The question of when Edith and I get married will have to wait until later.'

Rising to his feet, Fred shook the sand from the rug and folded it up. Lillian and her husband exchanged looks. Their sympathy was with Fred, but they were even more certain that Edith wouldn't wait much longer.

* * *

June and July were terrible months. Of nineteen dogs, fourteen died through haemorrhage, heart failure, infection and diabetes. More animals had to be brought in.

Fred and Charley went up to their rooftop eyrie to have a council of war. Charley had the record book with him, and they took the few dogs left up for a romp. The animals capered about, excited by their sudden freedom, then clustered round the two men, barking and wagging tails; but after a time, they lay stretched out, tongues lolling in the heat and eyes half shut.

Fred wanted to review the entries, and opened the pages showing the earliest results.

'This is the fifth of July. We ligated the pancreatic ducts in seven of the surviving dogs five weeks ago. I know I've said that there should be a wait of seven weeks before removing the section of pancreas left behind, but I think we might do an investigatory examination now. What do *you* think, Charley?' He was hoping for support because he simply could not wait any longer to see if his "idea" was working.

His assistant nodded. 'I agree. Must admit they all look pretty healthy to me. Shouldn't've thought that after so many of the others died. It'd be good to find out what's going on inside there. Do you want to start in the morning? I'll set out the instruments first thing.'

The sun was already hot early next day when Fred bent over the inert animal and removed the stitches. Charley swabbed blood away as Fred examined the exposed section of pancreas.

'Hell! Look at this!' he exclaimed. Clearly in view was a perfectly healthy looking pancreas. He had expected to find the surface decomposing, wrinkled and with some indication of a release of the inner secretion.

'The duct ties aren't tight enough. It hasn't worked – after all this time, it hasn't worked.'

The heartbreak and bitterness in his voice was plain. Catgut, the normal material used for closing wounds, and second nature to Fred after his experiences in the trenches, was no good for this application. It was too hard. Standing up, he mopped the sweat off his brow. The thermometer on the wall showed 97 degrees Fahrenheit.

'Look, Charley, we need something finer. There's a reel of silk in the cupboard over there. Bring it, and I'll try again. Might as well do it now while the animal is opened up anyway.'

The operation was repeated; the ducts looked much more secure. The wound was closed, and all appeared well.

'I think we'd better have a look at the others too,' Fred suggested. 'They may all be the same.' Of the other six, they found only three where the pancreases had degenerated in the way the surgeon wanted.

Of the four that had to have second operations carried out to tie the ducts more firmly, none lived more than a few hours; only three of the original seven were alive at the end of a disastrous week, but Fred tried to maintain a degree of optimism.

'This isn't the end of the road, Charley. These dogs have had *so* many complications that it's a wonder they lived this long... It's such a hard job to isolate the pancreas, let alone the ducts that surround it, but we *have* to prove that injecting our extract *will* bring down blood sugar. Let's concentrate on the three who've survived and whose pancreases are ready for the next stage. We'll remove their degenerated pancreases and make a serum from them. Next, we take the entire pancreases out from another couple of animals, and when their sugar levels rise, we give them injections of our extract and check blood sugar levels at every stage. When it falls, as I'm sure it will, we'll be able to persuade JJR that I'm right. He'll be back by September, and it'll take us up to then to allow the degeneration of another batch of pancreases anyway.'

Charley had been quiet while Fred was speaking.

'These dogs that have died. We could take their pancreases out now and make up an extract from them, even though they haven't degenerated?'

Fred nodded.

It was exactly what cousin Hipwell had suggested.

'Yes. We'll start with the fully degenerated ones first. Look out the instruments first thing tomorrow morning.'

After a couple of hours, three sets of pancreases lay on an enamel tray. The two men went up to the roof for a break. Fred lit up and explained what he wanted carried out next.

'It's five weeks now since these pancreases were fully ligated and we can see that they are certainly ready now. Slice them up as finely as you can and put the pieces into the mixture of salt and water that I'm making up. You'll know it as Ringer's Solution. Next, freeze the liquid and grind it in a mortar and pestle until it's as near powder as we can make it,' he continued. 'Then we'll filter it after it has thawed out. I'll remove complete pancreases from another two animals tomorrow. When they become sufficiently diabetic, we'll try an injection of our extract. How does that sound to you?'

Charley applied himself to the duties Fred had given him, and they returned to the roof for a spell to wait for the temperature of the solution to fall enough to allow it to be ground into flakes. Fred allowed the frozen crystals to thaw, and filtered the mixture through blotting paper. They watched the level rise as it dripped into a glass container.

It was an opaque shade of pink. Once the solution settled, Fred held it up to the light, then put it on the bench. A second batch was made up from fresh pancreases taken from the deceased animals.

'Well, that's it, Charley. Our first extract – ready for injection once we have a diabetic "patient". It'll need to be a dog meantime, but hopefully soon, a human being!'

On 30 July, Fred carried out a complete pancreatomy on one dog, a collie.

Fred opened the record book and entered the date and the serial number at the head of a fresh page.

'Start taking blood tests every hour, Charley. We'll soon know if this is going to work.'

1 August

Fred gazed at Charley's entries as the young man decanted the extracts into test tubes, carefully labelling the two types.

'Your tests show gradually increasing levels of sugar in our dog's blood now that there's no pancreas left. Now that we have a serum to try, we'll give it an injection when it reaches a higher level.

Charley heard the words with rising excitement.

'D'you think we might make history, then?'

Fred nodded. 'Yes I do.'

'We should give the extract a name, something to do with the Islets of Langerhans, don't you think? After all, that's where it comes from, isn't it?' Charley suggested.

'Yes, that's a good idea,' Fred thought for a moment. 'How about "Isletin"?'

'Right. I'll make all the entries in the records in future under that name,' Charley responded. Fred brought the animal and put it on the table.

With no pancreas and no Isletin, the blood sugar level rose quickly. When Charley recorded the third test at .50, he picked up a hypodermic syringe.

'What amount will I give?'

'Draw up 5cc,' Fred told him.

The Isletin was injected via a vein and an hour later, the blood sugar level had fallen to .20. Another 5cc of Isletin was injected and yet again, an hour later, the reading had dropped to .12. The two researchers exchanged looks. Fred could not stay silent.

'It's working! That's forty per cent lower than it was last time. Don't get too excited, but... Give it another shot. Use the other extract this time.'

Yet another injection was carried out. The dog was bright eyed and energetic, even running up to the roof and chasing the ball kept for the animals' exercise.

Digging about in the cupboard of the desk, Fred produced a bottle of champagne.

Filling two beakers, he handed one to Charley. Clinking his own against Charley's, his face broke into a broad grin.

'Here's to us, Charley. We're winning! I've kept this bottle hidden for the day this would happen. Have some more!' He held the glass up to the light, watching bubbles twinkle to the surface as fresh champagne was added.

'I think I'll stay all night – keep an eye on our miracle,' volunteered Fred.

'And I'll stay with you!' Charley turned to Fred. 'It's working. I can't believe it, but it's working!'

They shook hands so vigorously that the glass vessels standing on the bench tinkled and jangled as if applauding.

'We'll repeat the surgery on the second dog during the night, Charley. By the morning, its blood sugars will probably be the same as the collie's.'

The terrier did not do so well after the operation to extract the entire pancreas, and its blood sugar soared – to .60. After coming round after the anaesthetic, it was unable to stand.

'Give it a full syringeful, Charley. It should revive like the other one.'

One hour passed but the next test showed no fall.

'Give it another shot,' Fred instructed.

The result was catastrophic. The animal went into convulsions and died half an hour later. It had received repeated injections in attempts to reduce the exceptionally high blood sugars.

Had they studied their results more carefully, they would have realised two very important points. Firstly, that too *much* Isletin could kill just as readily as *no* Isletin, and that the serum obtained from fresh pancreases was just as effective as seven-week-old specimens…

As the weeks wore on, letters and reports were sent that described what was happening. Charley wrote to his fiancée, Margaret:

'The heat grows no less. I am tired because we work long into the nights and come back early in the mornings. There are some days I feel that we're on the brink of success. An animal responds perfectly to our injections of Isletin, and I feel great, then weary when

I see it sicken and die. Fred is certain that his idea is right, but even he gets depressed sometimes.

'We still have some time before the professor returns. I do hope we'll have better news by then. We leave the lab as seldom as possible. We eat steak and eggs fried on the Bunsen, with the bench as a dining table.'

The letter to Macleod from Banting was not much more optimistic.

'We have used an acidic suspension rather than a saline one. Our results are better. An alkaline suspension was not successful and, regretfully, more animals died. We are still having mixed results.'

JJR would have been surprised and disappointed that so few autopsies were recorded, but Fred was fairly relaxed over the deaths.

* * *

Day after day, night after night, variations were made in the composition of Isletin.

Acidic, saline, alcohol and many other suspensions were tried. A few weeks before Macleod's return, the collie was still well controlled, perky and bright. It was a particularly friendly beast, always affectionate and biddable.

Fred arrived at the lab at the end of the week, early, as usual. Charley was doing his entries at the desk and half turned.

'Fred, I think you should have a look at these figures. You took this dog's complete pancreas out a month ago. We've been giving it Isletin every time the blood sugar got higher. Well, this one's responding properly. There hasn't been a single relapse and it's *still* stable. Look.'

Taking the book, the surgeon studied the column. The graphs showed a pattern far steadier than any of the dozens before.

'I think we should give this one a name. She's quite a pet,' Charley said. 'And let her roam about the rooms, out of her cage.'

'Not a bad idea. Any name in particular?' Fred asked.

'How about Marjorie? It's the name of a girl I once fancied at school. All the entries in our records are by number, and I'll enter this one by number too, but there's nothing wrong with calling her by name here in the labs.'

The dog took to sleeping in a corner near the desk, where she could keep an eye on the men and get titbits more often than usual. Charley's tests showed that Isletin was controlling her diabetes perfectly.

She was always ready for a frisk about on the roof any time the men could take her up. Three weeks later, Fred looked over Charley's shoulder. He was making the latest entries in the book.

'I think Marjorie's the dog that's going to make history, Charley.'

CHAPTER 10

August – September 1921

Fred Banting's next letter to Professor Macleod was full of optimism and included requests for improved facilities in the rooms, someone to look after the dogs, and a number of proposals to further improve the performance of Isletin. He finished it with a compliment to his young assistant:

'Best has done extremely well in our research, and I would like to continue our work at the university over the rest of the summer vacation. He is willing to stay on with me if you are agreeable. Hoping to hear from you soon, and eagerly awaiting your return.'

The professor had no inkling of just how well their experiments with Marjorie were going because no mention was made of the dog. The letters emphasised the fact that Isletin was proving itself by the results of their tests. Failures were passed over lightly.

A day or two after the latest letter left, Charley raised an important point.

'Fred, we're going to run out of Isletin by Wednesday, and that's only two days away. What's more, we've got no degenerated pancreases left to make more for Marjorie's treatment. There aren't enough dogs left to get pancreases from either.'

The collie was sitting in the middle of the laboratory floor. At the mention of her name, she wagged her tail, went to the foot of the stairs, and looked towards them for a trip to the roof. Five weeks had passed since the injections began. Her wish was granted.

'OK, Charley, let's go upstairs. Bring Marjorie.'

The two leant over the parapet, Fred smoking a cigarette, Charley throwing the red rubber ball to Marjorie. She kept retrieving and fetching it back again and again. Fred finished his cigarette and made a sudden suggestion.

'The professor comes back late in September. It's now well into August and there's not enough time to remove pancreases from the dogs we have, wait seven weeks for them to degenerate, and have Isletin ready by the time he sees us again. I know from my farming days that the abattoirs have plenty of pancreases available – they're treated as offal and thrown out. Let's go along and see what's there.'

Their quest was successful. The men at the slaughterhouse had no hesitation in giving them as many pancreases as they wanted from newly slaughtered cows.

'We can let you have pig pancreases as well, if you like,' they offered.

'Stick to the bovine ones meantime,' Fred answered.

The men watched with curiosity as the two researchers departed with a couple of pails filled with them.

'Just make up a batch of Isletin the same way as we did before,' Fred told Charley.

'With that amount of pancreases, it'll make a fair quantity too.'

On the way back, 'Have you had a reply from the professor yet?' Charley asked.

'Yes. One came just this morning. I left it on the desk for you to read. He mentions the reports you sent him up to August the eighth as "encouraging and positive". He's agreeable to us working on the rest of the summer break too, which is fine. I've not told him about Marjorie – I'm keeping that as a surprise.'

Over the next few days, the collie's blood sugars remained controlled with injections of the 'new' serum. Meantime, various methods of refining Isletin were attempted. Some worked, others didn't, but they were happy enough just to potter about, paying particular attention to their star turn, the ever-energetic collie; and another, a black-and-white mongrel that had also reacted well over the last ten days.

Stella phoned the lab one day, late in the month.

'Are you free to come and see the professor on Friday?'

Banting borrowed cousin Hipwell's suit again.

September

Friday arrived and Banting made his way downstairs. Stella cast a critical eye over his appearance. Satisfied, she ushered him into the office.

The formalities over, the record book was opened, but Macleod did not make the kind of enthusiastic comment Banting was looking for.

'You've made progress, I see. I've looked carefully at your letters, Doctor Banting. I have to point out that the results of your serum would not yet pass the kind of questions you'll be asked at any meeting of experts. I'd rather you keep on with what you're doing until you can prove it effective *every* time. You're still having failures, I see.'

Banting's temper began to rise.

'Look here, Professor. The conditions under which we're working are quite appalling. When we wash the place, the floors leak water into the rooms below. The dogs smell so much because of the heat that we can hardly breathe. I've very little money coming in – I'm in the process of selling the house in London where I had my practice so's there'll be enough money to keep me alive. I can't afford a car. I even heat food over the Bunsen burner in the lab. I need some kind of income if the research is to go on.'

Professor Macleod's face was expressionless. He was stunned at such an outburst. The silence made Banting even more furious. Stella could hear what followed as his voice rose.

'You don't seem to realise we're almost there, about to put the name of Toronto University on everyone's lips! If you'll not give some help, I'll shift to the Rockefeller Institute or The Mayo Clinic!' He was tempted to tell the professor about Marjorie, but something held him back.

His listener did not stir in his chair, and looked directly at the red-faced Banting.

His calmness infuriated the surgeon even more. Macleod began to speak, coldly.

'I could hardly be expected to be aware of your financial situation. You never at any time mentioned money when you first came to see me – asking for facilities that you were given. And I *have* given advice and instruction to you both which, as far as I can see, has often been ignored. As far as transferring your activities elsewhere, equipment such as ours doesn't exist anywhere else. I think you would be better to choose your words more carefully. As far as you are concerned, Doctor, I *am* the University of Toronto.'

Banting's leather chair squeaked as he sat back. He forced himself to stay quiet and wait to see what Macleod would say next.

'I'll see what the university authorities can do about a salary for you. Help with the animal care will be provided. As far as the floor goes, you must remember that there is a new building under construction. This place will be demolished and the new one will replace it within a couple of years. Our funds are not limitless and there will be enormous expense involved in this, but I'll have the floor tarred meantime. That's about as much as I can do at the moment.'

Banting calmed down somewhat and the angry expression left his face, but his response was stiff.

'Well… I guess I can keep going then. I need to take a couple of days away to see to the sale of the house in London.'

The professor stood up. 'That'll be all right. I hope you get a decent price.'

He did not shake hands this time. Banting did not tell him that by the time the loan from his father and legal expenses over the sale were paid, there would be little or nothing left. Stella was at her desk as he stalked past, walking quickly. He neither spoke to her nor looked in her direction.

Charley was not in the lab room, but Marjorie gave Fred an excited reception. She looked up at him, red tongue hanging from her mouth, tail sweeping from side to side enthusiastically. The other mongrel had also been given a name – Towser, and she too was allowed freedom to roam around the rooms at will. The pair got on well with each other.

The sight of the living results of their labours swept his irritation away. He fetched a biscuit and threw it to them. Marjorie caught it expertly and crunched it up noisily, running to him for another, sitting, bright eyed, directly in front of him, but Towser got the next one. They were still playing with Fred when Charley arrived.

'How did things go then? Was the professor impressed?' he asked.

Fred was stroking Marjorie's head gently. She loved this, and thrust her head under his hand when he stopped, encouraging him to carry on.

'Things didn't, I'm afraid.' Fred's face darkened as a frown creased his forehead. 'Says our efforts wouldn't pass any close investigation. Gave me a row for neglecting his advice. Told him I'd close the research down and go elsewhere. D'you know what he said? Declared that *he* is the University of Toronto! Snapped at me! Told me to watch how I spoke. What a nerve!'

Charley noticed his partner's flushed face and was about to tell him to calm down, but Fred hadn't finished yet. 'I'll show that little son-of-a bitch that he's *not* the university! Keep special notes on all these cases where Isletin is doing well. Just wait! I'll show *him*!'

Charley was thinking quietly to himself. He was in an awkward situation. Macleod was his former tutor and a man for whom he had the greatest admiration.

Here was the professor, newly returned from Scotland, and already his senior's angry comments were making him feel uncomfortable.

All the animals were being treated with the 'new' Isletin originating from 'abattoir' pancreases. Not only Marjorie, but several other dogs continued to maintain blood sugars at almost normal levels, including Towser. She, like Marjorie, was affectionate and loveable. Deaths were far less frequent, but they *were* still happening. The few post mortems carried out marked these down to infection, heart failure and haemorrhage. Consistent success continued to elude them.

* * *

Charley noted that Edith Roach's engagement ring had not been dangling from Fred's watch chain for some time. His tactful enquiry did not tell him much.

'Fred, Margaret's birthday is next weekend. We're going to have a party at a hotel in town, and we'd like you and Edith to come. We haven't heard anything about her for weeks. How're things doing?' Fred stayed poker-faced.

'Thanks, but I can't tell you right away. I'm going to sell the house in London on Monday, so I'll probably be seeing her then.'

'You've had it on the market a while. Is this the deal being finalized then?' Fred nodded. 'Does Edith know about it?'

Fred looked at him gloomily. 'I'm afraid not. I just couldn't bring myself to tell her, but now I'll have to. She'll not be pleased, that's for sure.'

He had the use of a car to go to London. The plan was to arrive on Monday and see Edith in the evening. After spending the night in the Adelaide Street house, he would take any items of furniture left in the building, hand over the keys to the estate agent, and be back in the laboratory late on Tuesday night.

Fred's foreboding was correct. Edith and he had their meeting in London at a small café in the town centre – and it was not a happy one. It began with Fred breaking his news as gently as he could. A flush coloured her face. It was of anger.

'But why, Fred? We had plans for the house. We were going to live there when we got married...'

Fred looked over the table at her. Face flushed, tears brimming, she was not just angry, she was furious. Fred did his best to calm her down.

'Look, Edith, the future I planned for us is nearly here. The extract Charley and I have worked on all summer is succeeding. Even Professor Macleod agrees. He just wants a few more experiments carried out before we let the world know what we've done. Just a few more months. Please... please... believe me.' He reached out and took her hand, but she drew it away from him, taking a handkerchief to dab her eyes.

'I've heard all this before. I just don't know whether to trust you or not. We've hardly seen each other for weeks – just words on the telephone. Don't play with me like this. I've told you before that there's a limit to any girl's patience, and mine is running out.' Fred felt desperately sorry for her. Edith's distress was affecting him deeply.

'It's been such hard work: all this heat, all the failures, but we've got a dog – her name's Marjorie. She's stayed alive without a pancreas for twenty days, and we have another that's doing well too. We've called her Towser. The animals are alive because of our serum. We've even given it a name – Isletin.'

His voice became excited as the story poured out. In spite of her feelings, Edith began to respond sympathetically, but she was determined to force a decision.

'All right, Fred, I'll wait. But I have to have a decision on our future by January. I want to make plans for a spring wedding.' She looked at him directly for the first time that evening. 'You're not looking well, Fred. You're so thin. You're obviously not caring for yourself. Once we're married, I'll see you get some weight on.'

He reached for her hand again. This time, she let him hold it.

'I promise you'll have your wedding date soon, Edith. Just a little longer.'

He parted from his fiancée in a much more cheerful state. Edith was agreeable to giving him more time. Isletin was working well. Marjorie was full of energy. The professor had granted his requests. Life would be much better once some money started coming in. Everything was beginning to come together.

Next call was at Adelaide Street. There was very little furniture in the house. The night was not a comfortable one as he slept on the floor again, wrapped in a travelling rug.

In the morning, he walked through the rooms for the last time. The little desk and a chair were still in the consulting room. The sight of them brought back memories of the day he and Edith had explored the house for the first time. Although his optimism at the time had proved unfounded, he might have won out in the end.

Wonder if it might have been better just to let the practice build up like Bill Tew's? he thought. If I had gone that way, the odds are Edith and I would be married by now. Maybe I might even be a father.

Pulling his cigarettes out, he lit one and watched the curling smoke catch the weak sunlight flooding through the curtainless window, trying to persuade himself that his chances might yet take a turn for the better.

I'd never have got where I am now, on the brink of a triumph like this! The quicker I get back to Toronto and get on with my 'idea', the sooner Edith and I can wed.

The desk was put upside down on the back seat of the car, the chair placed inside the legs. He walked back to the front door and turned the key for the last time. Driving the short distance to the estate agent, he was told that there was a buyer, and 42 Adelaide Street became past history.

The lodging near Toronto University was cold and cheerless, but at least there was a comfortable bed. It had been a long drive, the borrowed car misfiring and noisy. Banting put in a good sleep before arriving at the lab later than usual.

Charley turned from the desk.

'Hi there. How did the house go? Did it fetch a decent price?'

'It's sold. Never mind the house! How are our two star turns?'

'They're fine, having a sleep on a rug on the roof. But really, it's too good to be true!'

Fred heaved a sigh of relief.

'What about the others?'

Charley's face fell. 'Not so good. Two more away, but no worse than usual.'

Fred was worried. 'We can't hope for a trial with a human diabetic at this rate. If word of the failures comes out, nobody'll ever believe a word I tell them. As long as this goes on, JJR will never agree to clinical treatment with Isletin. I think the deaths may be due to different responses to our extract. There are varying reactions to the same medicines by different sick people. It might be that the liquids in which we are suspending the extract aren't right for some of our dogs. We've been using cow pancreases. Why not try pigs?'

Fred sat down on a bench stool and lit the inevitable cigarette as Charley considered the suggestions.

'That's an idea, Fred. More work, but maybe you might be right.'

Three days later, another animal died, again after Isletin was given in large doses to combat high blood sugars. Fred was desolated. Marjorie was the only truly encouraging success, having lived for several weeks, although Towser was also faring well after fifteen days.

* * *

Arriving at the lab one morning he was met by a grim-faced assistant.

'Fred, I've bad news. Towser's dead. I found her in convulsions when I got here. I couldn't do anything to save her. She's on the operating table through there.'

Taken by surprise, Fred stopped in front of Charley.

'Dead? How can that be? She was fine when I left. In fact we had her up on the roof chasing the ball.'

Grim-faced, he was just taking off his jacket when Professor Macleod walked in. He was in a breezy mood.

'Ah, good morning. I thought I'd come to tell you about the arrangements I've made about the matters we were... were discussing... last week.'

One look at the two men made him see at once that something was wrong.

'Professor, I'm sorry, but you couldn't have come at a worse time. We had a dog that was doing tremendously well. It was found dying by Charley here when he arrived just a short time ago. I've just come in myself. This animal had had its pancreas totally removed and had lived for sixteen days. After careful blood sugar monitoring, the animal had been kept going by injections of our extract, fit, well and running around. I'd been keeping the news out of my reports to you until two months had passed, just to be absolutely sure, but now this...'

All three went next door to the operating room, where the dog lay on the table.

Fred stroked her head, taking her ear between his fingers and fondling it, something she had always liked. He almost expected her eyes to open.

'We'd both got very fond of her... She'd become quite a pet, this one.'

It was plain to the professor that they were deeply affected, even shocked at what had happened. Always masterly, he gave them the most sensible order.

'Right then, gentlemen. You need to carry out an autopsy. Get Doctor Fidlar to attend to it – you can't do this yourselves. It has to be independently done. Get him to do it now. Tell him what has happened, and ask him to pay particular attention to finding out if there's any part of the pancreas left in her. If there is, then this experiment will not persuade anyone that the animal was fully diabetic. The tiniest piece would produce the secretion and keep the dog alive. Come to my office when this is to hand. You can tell me about it, and we can talk about the other matters then too. I'm sorry you've had this setback, but it's not the end of the world. It certainly looks as if you're onto something now.'

Fred and Charley exchanged looks as Macleod left the room. Towser's death was a cruel disappointment.

Macleod turned at the door.

'By the way, I think it's time for you to give a lecture on your progress to the Physiological Club at the end of this month. If you would care to write up what you'd like to say, I'll present you to the assembly.'

Fred came to Macleod's office later that week; Stella rose to greet him. She could tell from his face that all was not well.

'Hi there, Fred. JJR's waiting for you. Just go in.' She tapped on the door and ushered the tall man forward. Macleod was writing notes.

'Come away in and sit down, Doctor.' Laying down his fountain pen, he clasped his hands in front of him.

'Well?' he asked. 'What did Professor Fidlar have to say?'

Banting's face was white as he answered. 'I have to tell you that there *was* a tiny section of the pancreas left.

'Oh dear, I *am* sorry to hear that. I know how disappointed you and Best must be.'

'I take it that this shouldn't be brought up at the talk at the Physiological Club?' Banting queried.

Macleod stayed silent momentarily. He was thinking ahead about the coming scenario.

'No, I don't think that would be a good idea. While the dog's survival is a magnificent achievement, there may be awkward questions asked. Until there is absolute proof that your extract works, discussing the latest disappointment would be unwise. Tell them about the researches so far, and you'll find that there's enough to discuss without including what people there would consider a failed effort. Produce evidence that your extract *does* have an effect on the sugar levels in diabetic animals. Just carry on with your work on the other dogs meantime.

'Now, to a more cheerful matter, I've made arrangements to appoint you as a lecturer attached to Professor Velyien Henderson's department. He knows you well, having tutored you in your student days here. He's doing a research project himself, but not related to yours in any way. Go and see him and he'll fill you in. There'll be little time taken up with university business – certainly not enough to interfere with your work in any way. It's only a title to justify your being paid. I've engaged a young boy to see to your dogs; and a contractor, who'll start next week, will seal the floor. Your salary will begin at the end of this month.'

A surprising remark followed. 'You'll also receive a lump sum: retrospective pay from the time you and Best started in mid-May.'

Fred Banting could not believe what the man behind the desk was saying. He had already made friends with the elderly Professor Henderson, who was working on the floor below theirs, so the news was welcome.

'There's just one thing more. Your reports refer to the serum as 'Isletin', but I am not too happy with the name. Perhaps we might discuss something different later?

With that, Banting stood to leave, putting out his hand. It was shaken warmly.

'Thank you so much, Professor. I am hoping that we can give

you good news before long.'

Macleod nodded. He felt the better for his actions, in a way reproaching himself for having been so unaware of the difficulties the two researchers had had to face.

Charley was relieved that the session had gone so well.

Every pledge the professor had made came about before the end of the month.

When Banting came into the lab the first week in December, he was wearing a new suit. Cutting the string on a parcel he was carrying, there was a crackle as the thick brown paper was unfolded. It contained a white lab coat fresh from the outfitter's shelf. When Charley remarked on the new clothing Fred told him, 'I needed these things and I paid the overdue rent to the landlady. And I gave her a liquid prescription…'

CHAPTER 11

November 1921

Fred could afford a night out drinking now that money was coming in. He could stand his hand, eat regularly and heat his rooms. He now had some opportunity to visit Edith more often, but this didn't happen because there was no encouraging news he could give her. The goals that they both longed for so deeply had not been achieved. Instead, he and Best carried on depancreatising dogs, trying the extracts in various suspensions to produce an Isletin that would extend the lives of at least two or three animals for a period longer than Towser. Doctor Fidlar's report following the post-mortem was put down as 'death due to toxic side effects'.

But there was another reason. Towser's sugar level had risen steeply the evening before her coma, so Charley increased the dose of Isletin. Yet again the researchers had overlooked the vitally important fact that too much extract could kill.

'What about grafting part of a healthy pancreas into a dog whose pancreas has been totally removed?' suggested Fred.

'Why not?' agreed Charley. 'It might repair what's left, or regenerate, after all.'

'We've nothing to lose,' said Fred, wearily. 'After all, we've made great strides so far, haven't we? Just a few more attempts…?'

There was no response from the young assistant. Success seemed tantalisingly close, but more 'ideas' were not forthcoming.

Macleod arrived again just as they were about to start, asking what they were doing. Best explained. Macleod shook his head.

'Look here, gentlemen, there's no point in doing such a thing. Grafting another bit of healthy pancreas will do nothing. No, I have to insist that your experiments proceed as you were doing before. Try using alcohol for suspending the extract until it evaporates.

Then use the Ringer's Solution to make up an injectable fluid. I'll see you at the lecture hall tomorrow, Doctor Banting. You'll have notes ready, I take it?'

Banting wore his new suit and had his hair cut for the lecture, an ordeal he was not looking forward to, but it was plainly something the professor felt timely. Walking along the echoing corridor of the Medical Building, he saw Macleod just disappearing through the doors marked 'Physiological Journal Club'.

There were about thirty men seated on the hard chairs, all talking to each other. Silence fell as the professor entered and made his way to a lectern sitting on top of a table.

Banting felt his heart beat faster, his muscles tense with nerves as he followed Macleod and sat on a chair next to him, facing the audience. The memory of his wretchedness when asked to read in front of his class at school returned vividly.

'Good morning, gentlemen,' Macleod began. 'You are aware that we have been striving to achieve the isolation of the mysterious secretion in the pancreas – the serum that converts carbohydrate in the diet to energy. It has been known for over seventy years that this fluid emanates from the Islets of Langerhans, cells within the pancreas. Many experts have been, and are trying, to isolate this fluid.

'I believe that we can prove that this has been done, and that when I hand over to my colleague here, Doctor Frederick Banting, he will explain how the process works.'

But he did *not* hand over to Banting. He went on to tell the audience about the research in such detail that the waiting speaker went into a panic. There's nothing left… unless they ask questions that'll give me a lead in… What can I say to them? he thought, perspiration breaking out on his forehead. Watching the man at his side, who was speaking without notes, he had to admit that the performance was nothing short of masterful, brilliantly delivered, but as the speech progressed, the word 'we' was repeated again and again.

It gave the impression to the listeners that the professor had been present at most stages of the research, but this was certainly not so. Lecture tours and summer holidays in Scotland constantly interrupted his presence at the university, but standard practice was to have the head of the department's name at the beginning of any programme, and this had been done in this instance.

At last, the professor stood aside.

'I have pleasure in introducing you to Doctor Frederick Banting, the researcher responsible for the remarkable findings I have just describd.'

Banting rose and took his place at the lectern on the same day as the 'Toronto Star' published an article complaining of the indiscriminate use of animals for research.

There was an active movement against the practice in the city – people who could become vociferous objectors. He made an eleventh hour decision to make use of the subject and by coincidence, the first questioner began with that topic.

'I can assure you that only dogs were used, that a minimum number was involved, and that no unnecessary suffering was imposed on them. Think of the fame that will accrue to Toronto University when the present series of experiments are proved successful…'

It was a great piece of sidetracking. There was a shuffle of feet and murmurs of approval. The enquirer fell silent. The professor answered almost every query that followed.

Banting simply did not have a chance and the audience dispersed, several shaking hands with Macleod on the way. Only two spoke to Banting – both personal friends. One was Velyien Henderson, but Fred, covered by embarrassment, was in a hurry. He stalked out of the room without a word to anyone else.

Frederick Banting was angry again. Angry at the way Professor Macleod had stolen his thunder, angry at the frequent use of the word 'we', angry at the way most of the listeners congratulated JJR rather than himself, the one who had started the whole show…

By the time he got back to the laboratory, his temper was white hot.

Charley came through from the theatre, going over to the sink to wash his hands.

As he dried them he turned to face the surgeon and asked how the lecture had gone.

'Bloody terrible!' Fred spat out. Best was surprised, but he had seen these outbursts before and knew to hold his tongue until his superior ran out of steam. But Fred was almost incandescent with fury this time. He could hardly speak.

'I've never heard anything like it… He's doing a good job of persuading people that *he's* the one who's getting places with Isletin. Didn't even like the name last time he deigned to speak to me, but he mentioned it several times tonight.'

In no mood to do any more work, and when Fred's face began to lose its redness, Charley made a suggestion. 'Look, let's go out and have a drink. You're in no state to do any more today. I don't think it'll do anything but good to get away from here for a bit. Prohibition hasn't shut down all the places where we can get some booze.'

Fred agreed, always finding that a good drink made everything look much better.

They sat with pint beer glasses in front of them. 'The last thing I needed was what's just happened,' Fred observed.

'I think we'd be better talking about something else, and I've got some interesting news to give you,' said Charley. Fred took a mouthful of beer and laid the glass down.

'Well? I hope it's good news. If it isn't, don't tell me.'

'While you were away at the conference, there was a visitor. His name's Collip, James Bertram Collip, to be precise. He's *very* interested in the diabetes research.'

Fred sat up immediately.

'I know him. He's from Alberta University and he's spending six months here with the professor. Got funding from the Rockefellar Foundation, lucky devil... What did he want? Did the professor send him?'

'Well, he didn't say anything about that, Fred, but he'd like to have a talk with you.'

Fred lit a cigarette. He spoke slowly and thoughtfully. 'He might be the very man. Professor Macleod introduced me to him the day we started. He's a professor – graduated in biochemistry here in Toronto, and specialises in glandular secretions. Yes. The more I think about it, the more I feel we might ask him to join us. It all depends on JJR, of course. I'll try and have a talk with him tomorrow.'

Charley ordered another two pints. When he brought them back, Fred was smoking again and there was a furrow on his forehead.

'There's another problem. We've used up nearly all the degenerated pancreases we had in store. If we're to keep doing what the professor wants, we'll have to suspend operations meantime. If Collip's only here for six months, then two are gone already and we'd have to wait seven weeks or so for the next batch of pancreases to be ready.

There's the Christmas holidays too. Collip's married and has a family. He'll want to go home for that, don't you think?'

Charley nodded glumly, but Fred was thinking things out.

'The first thing's to see what Macleod says. Our own results aren't very promising again. Perhaps a fresh approach might come up with something.'

Professor James Bertram Collip joined the team on 12 December, working in a laboratory in the Pathology Department attached to the nearby Toronto General Hospital.

CHAPTER 12

12 December 1921

James Collip's good looks made people look twice at him. Tall, his boyish and forceful features were striking, and a direct look as he spoke to anyone made a deep impression.

In fact he was shy and sensitive. One of his greatest pleasures was time spent in the laboratory.

A nickname that described his methods was 'The Bathtub Scientist' because of a reputation for throwing everything and anything in the pot when carrying out experiments. Another pleasure was being with his family back home in Alberta.

Fred Banting's optimism about the 29-year-old Professor Collip was justified. In fact, few could have been more suitable to help develop the project. His BA (Honours) in Physiology and Biochemistry had been gained at Toronto University in 1912, an MA in 1913 and by 1916, a Ph.D. In 1915 he became a lecturer in physiology at Alberta University, and by 1920 was in charge of a new department of biochemistry there.

An active researcher in a variety of blood disorders, he *was* to bring a different approach to the problems the others were encountering.

The four met together at Professor Macleod's office the day before Collip joined the team.

'Hi there, Fred.'

Collip greeted Banting, advancing with hand outstretched to the surgeon, then to young Best.

'I'm pleased that Professor Collip is able to spend some time with you,' Macleod remarked to the two men. 'You've met before, gentlemen. I've allocated a place for him to work in the hospital building since there's not much room where you two are. It's near enough to enable you to keep in close touch. Go over to the lab and fill him in on what's happening, if you please. Now, I've made out some more notes on the next steps in the research – Professor Collip refining the extract that you will continue to produce. Doctor Banting, d'you agree with that?'

Banting nodded.

Best stayed silent. In fact, knowing Fred as he did, he was not sure that relationships would always be so good.

Macleod rose from the desk.

'Right then. Off you go. I think we should try to meet together at lunch whenever that's possible. It'll be easier to keep me advised as to progress that way.'

James Collip read through the records that Fred put down on the desk.

Even with regular cleaning there was still a smell permeating the room, only slightly changed by having the odour of strong disinfectant predominating.

James's nostrils twitched but he said nothing.

'The results vary a bit,' he remarked, turning a page. 'Some remarkable, some not so good, but it's obvious you're on the right track. We'll need to be smart off the mark though. D'you know that the Romanian, Paulescu, is doing the same sort of thing as you? He's already on the brink of taking out a patent.'

Fred looked up sharply at Charley.

'You've been reading his papers. You told me he was far behind us. How is James's story so different?'

Charley shrugged. 'The papers are in French... I didn't do very well at languages at school.'

It was later found that Charley had seriously misinterpreted some of the data. Far from reading that Paulescu was well ahead in his research work, his impression was that their own results were more advanced.

It was at that moment that the pair realised time was not on their side. They had delayed far too long due to their own inexperience. Macleod had been away during the most critical period of their work, and it was as well that a scientist like Collip had teamed up with them.

Collip decided on the very first day that he would try to make up some pancreatic extract using the same method as Banting and Best. The first move was to send his lab boy to the abattoir. The lad returned with material in a glass jar, and James started work on the contents at once. The extract was ready the next day.

He chose rabbits for most of his experiments because it was much easier to take blood for testing from veins in the ear. His intention was to inject the extract to one of the little animals without removing its pancreas.

To his surprise there was no affect whatever. Repeated attempts made no difference to the blood levels. He went over to see Banting and Best.

'I don't think my first experiment is working properly. I used the same techniques as you, but there's something wrong with this whole piece of work.'

Fred looked at the small tube of Isletin that James had brought with him. 'It's the wrong colour for a start. What did you put on the note for the boy to collect? It should be pancreases.'

James's face grew red.

'I thought it was sweetbreads.' What the boy had brought in the jar was a quantity of thyroid glands… Charley put a hand over his mouth. Soon all three were laughing.

'Better not tell the professor about this one,' James said, as Fred lit a cigarette.

Over lunchtime meetings, Macleod listened intently as Collip related the results of his efforts.

'I started off with whole beef pancreases, making fundamentally what you've called 'Isletin'. I found it reduced the blood sugar of rabbits immediately, just as you predicted, Fred.' He made no comment about the gaffe over trying to make successful extracts from the wrong organs.

'By doing this experiment on non-diabetic animals, I found that an overdose sent them into violent convulsions and they died soon after. Examining the livers and other organs, it became plain that an overdose of the extract was the cause of death.'

Neither Banting nor Best made any comment. It had taken their new colleague a matter of days to find something that with proper post-mortems, they should have detected long ago.

* * *

By the second week in December, it became more and more obvious to the two original researchers that Collip was far superior to either of them in laboratory techniques.

'We'll need to keep an eye on our James,' Fred remarked to his assistant one morning.

Charley went to Fred's aid right away.

'Why? We've proved that Isletin works. James was instructed to *refine* our extracts, not reinvent them. JJR advised us to prove it by keeping a depancreatised animal alive with Isletin, and Marjorie's doing all right, isn't she?'

They kept her going on a quantity of Isletin made before Towser died, but there was not much left.

'Let's make a real big quantity this time,' suggested Fred.

Charley looked at him silently. He was wondering why Fred had seemingly abandoned the suggestion from the professor that Collip should do the refining of Isletin.

'Get as many pancreases as you can from the abattoir.'

Charley took off his white coat and left.

When he came back, they set to work, making over 1200cc of Isletin, which included 500cc of acid alcohol. To their dismay, it was a failure. Trying it out on several depancreatised dogs, the sugar in their blood mounted steadily every hour. Increasing the amounts injected did nothing to halt an inexorable rise.

'This is terrible, Charley. Look, make up another batch, but use plain alcohol this time. Evaporate it with the fan playing over a flat dish. We'll use the Ringer's Solution once again to dissolve the powder. That should finish up the same as the successful batch we're using on Marjorie.'

It had no effect. Exasperated and worried, his face showed the depth of Fred's concern.

'Charley, I think we should take a rest. It's Christmas after all. Let's go down and have a few beers and maybe we'll feel better. Something's wrong and I just don't know what.'

Apart from coming in to give Marjorie her injections and take her out to the campus for walks, no further work was mounted until another lecture had to be prepared.

'I think it's time that you told the American Physiological Society about your work, Doctor Banting,' Macleod announced one day. 'This conference will be held at Yale University in New Haven. You'll need an overnight stay. Most of the well-known experts will be attending. One of them will be the research director of the Eli Lilly pharmaceutical manufacturers. They're one of the biggest in the country. His name is George Clowes. Try to get him interested – that's a company that could help a lot. I'll be chairing the meeting and I'll introduce you as I did before, then you can give the paper.' The memory of what happened at the last attempt filled Banting with foreboding.

It was worse, *far* worse. People asked questions so complex, even rude, that Fred Banting was completely out of his depth.

He wrote in his diary, 'When I was called upon to present our work, I became almost paralyzed. I could not remember a thing, nor could I think properly. I had never spoken to an audience of this kind before. Overawed, I did not present it well.'

The inevitable took place. Macleod took over. He was an experienced platform performer, assured and well able to answer the fierce critics who sat before him. Banting occupied a chair at the back of the platform, red-faced and embarrassed.

Later that week, the professor told a colleague what had happened.

'There was a large number of experts there: people like Fred Allen, the 'starvation diet' man; Elliot Joslin, a man whose life has been spent on treating diabetics, especially children. There were others too: Carlson; Kleiner; and George Clowes, the research director from Eli Lilly.

'The trouble began with a comment from Anton Carlson, whose experiments have been similar to ours. He remarked that his dogs lived for a considerable time after depancreatisation without treatment of any kind. Young Best made a rather tactless comment by asking Carlson if he was certain that the pancreases had in fact been removed completely. Best knew, of course, about the post-mortem that Doctor Fidlar performed on a dog that had lived for many weeks under treatment with Isletin, and that he had found a tiny fragment of its pancreas left. Even although it was impossible that such an amount could possibly be functioning, the experiment was declared void in view of it.

'It was then that poor Banting went to pieces. He lacks confidence in front of a sometimes sarcastic audience, and his country accent doesn't help. It was like watching wolves slaughtering a lamb. The man's basically a surgeon, not a research chemist. That's why I had a student in his fourth year, young Charles Best, join him to do the lab work.

'It's a pity that both lack experience in the diabetes field. Some of the questions were so complex that I felt compelled to answer them myself. I kept emphasising that enough proof was available, that Isletin *does* reduce blood sugar levels, but some wouldn't even accept that there *is* a secretion in the pancreas that converts carbohydrate into energy. There're always critics present at that sort of conference who try to put the talker off their stride – very easy to do in Banting's case. One man was impressed though: George Clowes. He came over to the hotel after the meeting and, in view of his importance, I agreed to see him privately.

'He offered Eli Lilly's help in developing Isletin at their laboratories in Indiana.'

He stopped to fill the pipe, then after it had settled, continued.

'They have the best-equipped facilities in the USA, but I told him that our investigations were not yet ready. If companies like that get involved, they stand to make millions.

'We're not at that stage yet, but I feel that once we *are*, it's a company like that we'll need for bulk production. This may not be too much longer. Our new man, Collip, from Alberta, is making rapid progress in refining the secretions that Banting and Best are extracting. I think it may soon be possible to try a clinical test with his product, but Banting keeps pressing me to try *his* extract, Isletin. So far I've resisted, although he and Best have certainly worked very hard since May.

'Trouble is, they seem to have come to a dead end. The treatment with Isletin isn't consistent, and their results irregular. But he does keep trying.'

James Collip was working in his lab, producing a type of Isletin, but using a different method. He decided to leave a small amount of alcohol present – something the others had removed altogether.

One evening, the latest batch produced spectacular findings. Every test proved effective. Again and again, the lowering of the animals' blood sugar took place.

With mounting excitement and continuously successful results to report, the others at the table during the lunchtime conference noticed that Collip's voice was raised and agitated.

'I've got a depancreatised Airedale over there.' He lifted a piece of meat on his fork and waved it over the plate to emphasise each point.

'It became severely diabetic, losing weight and energy by the day, but during the last three days on the refined serum, the animal got its energy back. The blood sugar has fallen substantially and I can keep it under control according to the amount injected.'

The others stopped eating. The professor laid down his cutlery.

'You're quite sure of this? Have you made up enough to continue tests for long enough to verify your results?'

Collip shook his head. 'I'm only making sample quantities at the moment. I've finished that batch, but all the results were positive. I'll make more, never fear. I'll make more.'

He did not tell them that he had not kept a note of the formula.

Once back in the lab, Fred turned to Charley.

'I knew it! They're trying to cut us out. Look at the way Macleod commandeered the last two lectures... I couldn't get a word in edgeways. And as for James, well, he's just repeating the work we did months ago. They're great pals, Macleod and Collip. I'm telling you, they're trying to squeeze us out.'

His listener stayed quiet. After being at the last meeting at New Haven, he knew that Fred could not have survived without the professor.

The setbacks of the last week exhausted them. They left the lab for a Christmas holiday, but as soon as Banting was able to meet with the professor, he tried once more to persuade him to allow Isletin to be used on a patient.

'We know that one batch of Isletin is effective. After all our disappointments, would you allow us a clinical trial? Please say you will.'

Macleod could see how deeply Banting needed a break, but the fact that all Banting's activities had been performed under his

authority worried him. After a moment's thought he made a decision. It was to prove a disastrous one.

'There's a young lad in the diabetic ward. He's fourteen and he's
dying – down to sixty-five pounds in weight. All right, go ahead.
His name's Leonard Thompson. I'll speak to Walter Campbell over
at the hospital in the afternoon. You know him. He's the man in
charge of the clinic there.'

Banting's eyes lit up. He could not wait to get back to tell Charley.

12 January 1922

Fred's excitement drove him to light cigarette after cigarette. The
room reeked of tobacco smoke. He almost spilled the precious
Isletin that he was trying to decant into a test tube to take over to
Toronto General Hospital. He managed it eventually, and thrust a
cork into the neck.

'Well, Charley, if you're ready, let's go. When we come back we
may be on the way to fame.'

Charley was deeply affected too, his face tense and drawn.
'Shake on it,' he said, sticking his hand out.

They took only a few minutes to cross to the big hospital block
and mount the stairs to the diabetic ward. A sister was sitting at the
nursing station desk.

'Wait here please,' she said, rising to go into the ward. She closed
the door behind her, leaving the pair standing, with Banting holding
the tube of Isletin. He had hoped that Macleod would have been there
but almost before the ward doors had stopped swinging, Duncan
Graham, Professor of Medicine and in charge of the medical wards,
strode towards them. His eyes were cold and his manner equally so.

'Good morning gentlemen. Doctor Banting, I have to tell you
that you are not permitted to administer medication to any patient
under my care. You have neither standing nor any appointment
within the hospital, and for me to allow anyone to do such a thing
would be against every rule prevailing here.'

White with anger, Banting struggled to control his fury.

'I understood from Professor Macleod that I could expect your co-operation in treating the boy Thompson with this serum, Isletin. It may well save his life.'

'I'm sorry, Doctor. What I said was that you personally could not perform the injections. I did not say that the medication was not to be given. I'll bring Doctor Campbell, who looks after the diabetic patients here, but I absolutely forbid either of you to enter the ward or approach the patient.'

There was obviously no protest that either of them could make against so firm a stance.

Just with that, two others approached the group, almost as if they had been ready and waiting.

'I'm Walter Campbell. This is Doctor Jeffrey.' Neither made any effort to welcome the researchers.

'I believe you understand the situation,' continued Campbell. The matter had obviously been discussed before the two men arrived. 'If you give us your extract, I'll supervise its administration. Doctor Jeffrey will see to this. I think you might as well leave meantime. There's nothing for either of you to do here.'

Banting was still controlling his temper with difficulty. 'We'd like to have blood and urine specimens for testing over in our own department.'

The answer remained totally unyielding. 'These are the property of the hospital. No, I'm afraid you cannot have anything at all. We will do all the tests necessary and advise you in due course. Now please leave.'

The pair turned slowly and trudged back down the stairs. Both were taken aback at their reception, frustrated and furious.

Professor Graham took the tube from Jeffrey and held it up to the light.

'Thick, brown muck!' he remarked, holding the tube in his fingertips.

Back in their rooms, Fred rounded on Charley. He could hardly speak.

'Can you believe this? How dare they exclude us from treating that boy. After all the work we've done…' He collapsed into the chair at the desk and hid his face in his hands. Charley felt desperately sorry for him, but there was nothing either of them could do but wait until a messenger came over from the hospital.

In fact, Charley thought, Professor Campbell had been quite correct in refusing them access to Leonard Thompson. The rule was well known, but he did not feel that Fred's temper would be improved if he attempted to tell him.

The next morning, 13 January, Fred sat about the room, chain smoking, occasionally going to give the dogs a piece of biscuit. The passage door was left wide open to allow anyone approaching to be heard.

At ten thirty, Fred could wait no longer.

'D'you think we should go back over there and see what's happening? I can't believe there's no change in the boy's condition. What d'you think?'

Charley took only a moment.

'I think you should hold on. The people there'll just be as deliberately unpleasant as they were yesterday. Go up on the roof and get some fresh air. I'll wait here in case – '

Just with that there was the sound of footsteps outside. Someone was coming. The footsteps stopped at the open door and there was a knock on the jamb. A staff nurse came in. 'I've brought a note from Doctor Campbell.'

Fred seized it and spread it out on the desk so that Charley could also see it.

It did not give the news they needed so desperately. Fred read it out slowly.

'12 January. Leonard Thompson.

'Two injections were made, fifteen cc of Isletin – seven and a half cc into each buttock. One hour later, the patient's blood sugar had fallen only marginally The Rothera test for ketones continued strongly positive. No clinical benefit was evidenced.'

The last sentence showed only too clearly that, in the opinion of Duncan Campbell and his colleagues, Isletin had failed.

'What are they saying?' fumed Banting. 'The evidence is there. The boy's sugar levels fell after an injection of our extract. It was less than half the amount I would have recommended for one of our dogs. That blood reading is only a fraction more than the German researcher, Zeulzer, found in 1912. No wonder!' The messenger was still there, waiting quietly. Charley asked the most important question of all.

'Have the injections been stopped then?' The reply confirmed their worst thoughts.

'Doctor Campbell noted that an abscess had risen at the point where one of the injections was made. He says the boy is deeply ill and shouldn't be made more uncomfortable by carrying out further treatment. He ordered that no further treatment should proceed. I'm sorry. I've been allocated the duty of caring for him myself, and I had hoped that your Isletin might save him.'

She turned away, and the sound of her footsteps faded away along the corridor. Utter silence prevailed until Charley touched Fred's arm.

'C'mon. Time to leave for the day. Let's buzz off down to the speakeasy. They're open all day and all night too.'

Banting was silent until they sat down with full glasses in front of them.

'You know as well as I do that if they'd carried on, that boy would have recovered.'

'Look, Fred, try not to worry so much. We'll get there, but it'll take a bit more time…'

CHAPTER 13

January 1922

Frederick Banting was in one of his self-destructing moods. The fixation that everyone's hand was against him started his day and ended it. Mention of the name Macleod made him act like a newly lit firework, fizzing with indignation and exploding with unpleasant remarks made without thought. His was a dislike rapidly developing into hatred. Anyone who would listen, friend and foe alike, were subjected to his tirades – 'professors with no ideas... professors who pretend to help, claim all the credit and do nothing... people who only want to steal other's work...' On and on it went. There was never doubt in the listener's ears as to who was being referred to. Charley was finding life with his associate extra difficult, and tried to lift Fred's morale whenever he could.

'There's so little to do,' groaned Fred one morning. 'We can't do much more than collect pancreases from the abattoir, process them and hand the material over to Collip.'

'*And* keep Marjorie alive!' added Charley, manfully doing his best again.

Fred put his coat on.

'I'm fed up; can't hang about this way. There are some things I want to get in town. Just tidy up a bit, then you can take the rest of the day off.'

He had just left when there was a tap at the door. The man who stood there looked vaguely familiar to Charley.

'Hi! My name's Fred Greenaway. My card.'

'News Desk: *Toronto Star*', it read. Charley looked at the piece of cardboard, puzzled.

'And what brings you here?' he asked.

'I hear there's been work going on here – some kind of cure for diabetes. You'll be Doctor Banting? The man in charge of things?'

Charley put him right as to the identities of the team.

'Yes, we are conducting research. It's into a treatment to counteract the present situation with regard to diabetes. It's *not* a cure. You'll know that anyone diagnosed as suffering from it hasn't much of a future.'

Greenaway got out his notebook and flipped it open. 'Right, Doctor. Would you like to enlarge on that? I'm told that a boy has been given your serum over in the diabetic ward. How's he doing? The staff at the hospital won't tell me anything.'

Charley realised he ought to be directing the reporter to someone more senior.

'Look, I don't think you should be asking me these questions. I'll see if Professor Macleod is free to see you. Wait here please. By the way, don't address me as Doctor. I'm just plain Mister.'

When Stella Clutton told the professor that there was a newsman waiting to see him, his heart sank. The last thing he wanted was the press sniffing around, but she told him that the man seemed to know enough to scent a headline story. She was told to show him in. Shaking his hand, the professor gestured the visitor to a chair.

'Now look, Mr Greenaway, our researches are not yet complete. To even hint that there is hope for the thousands of diabetics in this country, let alone millions in the world, will bring an avalanche of sufferers wanting help. We simply couldn't cope with that, especially since there is no certainty that we have a potent serum. There may be side effects, there may be people with whom it is successful, others not.

'We don't know anything that would warrant saying there's a cure. We are working intensively with the hope that some day we may be able to help people who have diabetes live normal lives.'

Greenaway asked if many others were trying to find a way of treating the disease.

'Yes, hundreds, all over the world. At the New Haven lecture, we were able to report that the path we are following is a little more likely to achieve what we are trying to do, that was all. We need time and peace to continue our investigations until we're sure of safety and health to our patients. I beg of you, don't build the story up and give them false hope at this stage. Now if you don't mind, I've a lot to do.'

It was clear that the professor would not add anything to the statement. Greenaway promised to keep the article low key, and rose to depart.

The *Toronto Star* printed the feature on 16 January. When Banting read it, he erupted again with fury.

'Just look at this, Charley! How many 'WE's' can you count? Who's the "we"? It certainly isn't Macleod, and it wasn't James Collip until a few weeks ago. You and I are barely named anywhere either. What a damned cheek! It's obvious Macleod concocted this to put himself on top.'

He tore off the lab coat and thrust his jacket on.

'I'm going up on the roof. Don't come up.'

Storming out of the room, he knocked a stool over without stopping to pick it up. He wanted to be alone with his thoughts.

* * *

Professor Macleod had heard nothing about Fred Banting's rantings until his close friend Duncan Graham came over from the hospital one day. Banting had just been letting him know about his feelings.

'I'm sorry to tell you this, JJR, but your man Banting has just left me. He's saying some pretty terrible things about you. Says you're stealing his ideas, that you're claiming the credit for the discovery of Isletin, says his name's not quoted in the *Star* feature, and a lot of other things as well. I think you need to see him, and pretty quick too. There's no reason for his behaving this way. After all, you let him set up his project here, gave advice, saw he got a salary and so on, didn't you?'

Macleod was surprised and saddened.

'Can't think why he feels that way. I didn't give names during the interview with the *Star* reporter because that would simply have set the newshounds loose on them all. That wouldn't have helped anything. I'm expecting the mailbag to get bigger by tomorrow. The mail's already growing – letters from diabetics, relatives of diabetics, doctors who treat diabetics. All want information we can't give. I'll try to see Banting soon.'

Duncan Graham grimaced. 'I'd make it very soon, if I were you. He's talking to anyone who'll listen!' As soon as Campbell left, Stella was asked to have Banting come to the office.

He was not invited to sit down. Shamefaced and apologetic, he stood shifting from one leg to the other while Macleod explained clearly what had been said to the journalist, and the reasons for keeping clear of names. The *Star* lay open on his desk.

'There's no truth in what you are saying, Doctor Banting. You've been given all the assistance I could give you – and you know it. I didn't expect this kind of reaction from you, of all people. I think you've been working too hard. Take a break away from here. Go home for a few days, see your fiancée, relax a little. There are four in the team – no more, no less – so in order to make this clear, in any future speech, interview with the press or written papers, I will place all four names in their alphabetical sequence, your own first, then Best, Collip's, then my own. Now can we agree on that?'

Banting nodded and made an attempt to apologise.

'I'm sorry. There have been misunderstandings and I admit they have angered me. Tale-telling results in exaggeration, and I'll try to see that these situations don't arise again.'

Macleod replied. 'With only a small group involved in this research, the last thing I want is newspaper men intruding on our work – and they will if they get half a chance. Then we'll have hordes of diabetics descending on us at the hospital. We don't have the staff to cope with that kind of thing. I *did* interview this man, but I certainly didn't give any names at all to him – although he'd already got yours, and Best's already. I emphasised during the short interview that he should *not* quote our identities, but the press is a law unto itself, believe me!'

As the door closed behind him, the professor heaved a sigh of relief. One of his deepest dislikes was becoming embroiled in confrontations like this. He was hoping the interview had solved the problem.

It had not.

Setting out the events of the day in his diary later, Banting wrote, 'The professor thinks I've been working too hard, need a holiday. He smoothed the problem with a sticky candy.'

* * *

During the first half of January, James Collip was hard at work. Speaking only curtly to the others when they brought some of their extract over to him only added to the suspicions festering in Fred Banting's mind. When James Collip did not show up for almost a week at the lunch breaks, his doubts grew even deeper.

Collip's week had, in fact, been spent alone in his isolated laboratory. All day and half the night, he attempted again and again to produce a completely effective solution. Varying the mix – less acid, more acid, more alcohol, less alcohol – the pattern followed Banting and Best's: sometimes it worked, sometimes it didn't.

On the night of 16 January, he altered the mixture once more, perhaps guessing, perhaps calculating, but the result was certainly effective.

There was a consistent series of satisfactory lowerings of blood sugar in depancreatised rabbits and a dog.

As test after test proved successful, a thrill of excitement began to course through him. As each test confirmed the degree of control over the presence of sugar in the blood, his heartbeats became faster and faster.

'If this is triumph at last, mankind will benefit beyond all belief.'

Someone had written these words somewhere, and they were the first to come to his mind. The overwhelming realisation of what they meant made the blood pound in his head. He felt dizzy and stood up, holding on to the desk, his mind in turmoil.

Five days of hard, concentrated effort, with scarcely a break, showed in his face. He had neither shaved, nor slept more than a few hours at a time.

The news was so tremendous that communication with someone – anyone – had to come next.

He had learned that a patient had already been given Isletin. The news took him by surprise. Disappointed that neither the professor nor any of the others had said anything about it – even that the trial had failed, he decided to stay silent. There was a job to do. It was going better than anyone could have hoped for. Charles Best had been a party to the Isletin trial, but Collip had to talk to *someone* about his stupendous success and Best, he knew, was in the building. He should be the first to know.

Lifting his jacket from its hook, he set off for the university building. To his surprise, both Banting and Best were in their lab.

Fred was smoking; Charley was leaning against the bench. The phials and tubes sparkled – there had been plenty of time to clean them over the past few weeks. Collip walked in and went over to them. They noticed his haggard face and the stubble on his chin.

'I've cracked it…' he said calmly. They both stared at him, speechless for a moment. Fred turned white. '…and I'll have enough made up to supply the ward patients for a few weeks.'

'What? How?' snapped Fred, getting up from the chair.

'I'm sorry. I've decided not to tell you.'

Fred took a step forward. Charley moved closer to where Fred was glaring at James, almost eyeball to eyeball, his attitude threatening. It looked as if Fred was about to lash out at the other. Charley forced himself between them.

'Steady on, you two! This'll do no good at all.' Collip turned away, towards the door.

'I'm tired out. Good night,' he mumbled. His footsteps clicked away along the passage. Fred turned to Charley.

'Well, that's it. We've lost the place. Might as well go home. Maybe I'll see you tomorrow, maybe I'll not…'

* * *

There was little contact between members of the team after the confrontation. Collip carried on making his own extracts made from beef pancreases brought to him directly from the abattoir. Banting and Best did the same, even adopting Collip's techniques to produce their Isletin.

The dog, Marjorie, stayed fit on her injections of it. Collip's Airedale stayed in good health, treated with his refined secretion. The lunchtime meetings continued, but they were sparsely attended. Seldom were all four present.

Macleod was aware that trouble had broken out – trouble so serious that the team had split up. Also that Fred Banting's criticisms of him were becoming more and more fierce in spite of his promise to stop, and that it was rumoured that Collip was considering applying for patent rights for his successful extract. The professor was also deeply disturbed about the disaster that had taken place with Banting's and Best's trial on Leonard Thompson.

The fact that Collip had told him about the positive effect his extract was having on the rabbits must have made him regret that he had given Banting approval for a clinical trial, especially when the entire research was being undertaken with his own name listed as heading the team. This was the established pattern in such projects conducted in the university.

Macleod had another call from his friend at the hospital, Professor Graham. It was about Leonard Thompson.

'He's much worse, I'm afraid. I fear he's not going to live much longer. Is there any progress in finding an effective pancreatic extract? I have to agree with Banting that there *was* a slight reduction in the patient's blood sugar after Isletin was administered, but it was so small. Because an abscess appeared at the injection site, I decided not to proceed with the treatment, to save further discomfort to the boy. The parents are deeply distressed and fear that he may die just as an effective treatment emerges, which would be tragic. We all pray for a breakthrough soon enough to save his life and that of the others in the ward. Is there anything I can say to Thompson's mother and father?'

Macleod filled his pipe slowly and deliberately. The process gave him time to think even more carefully than usual. There had been enough mistakes made so far, and there must be no more. He sat back and spoke slowly.

'If the parents are agreeable, I think we can offer another course of injections around the twenty-second of this month. We should have Collip's extract available by then and we'll try his this time. This is the nineteenth. Can he last that long, d'you think?'

Campbell nodded thoughtfully. 'He's not likely to stay alive more than a couple of days, JJR. I know you'll tell me the moment you can help him.'

The team was called to another conference in Macleod's office later in the week. They arrived with serious expressions; there was no conversation going on between them.

'Coffee, gentlemen?' he offered, hoping that the atmosphere might be warmed a little, but all the heads shook.

'Well, do sit down.' No one would look him in the eye; in fact they all seemed to be finding the pattern on the carpet singularly interesting. There was still utter silence between them as they made their way to chairs set out for them close to the front of the desk.

Macleod sat back and began.

'I've called this meeting because I have to do something about the behaviour prevailing between you. I understand you are working individually, which is not the arrangement I thought we had agreed in December.

'Now that'll not do at all. I would like to suggest that we all sign a declaration that we will *not* act independently in future.

'Consultation *must* take place between each of you and myself at every stage of the work in hand. I intend that a contract be established with the university's in-house company, Connaught Antitoxin Laboratories, with the objective of their manufacturing a product, once refined from its present state, that will effectively lower the blood sugar of a diabetic patient. The contract will not allow any member of the team to take out patent rights in their own name.

'I've drafted one out in consultation with Professor Fitzgerald, the director of Connaught; and the university lawyers. It's not lengthy, and I would like you to read it now, then sign it.'

Stella, who had been sitting at the side of the professor's desk taking minutes, rose to her feet and handed the documents to the grim-faced listeners.

After a short period, Fred Banting spoke first, having spotted the advantages at once. Any attempt by James Collip, or anyone else for that matter, as regards patent rights, would be impossible. Collip was due to end his six months sojourn at the University of Toronto in a few weeks, and return to Alberta. It was entirely possible that he might be encouraged by his own Alma Mater to patent his extract there, giving Alberta University the credit rather than Toronto. Such a thought horrified Fred, hence his prompt desire to sign the professor's paper.

Best followed, then Collip, and finally Macleod. Stella took the documents and put them in a cardboard folder.

'How about some of my coffee now?' The aroma was enough to persuade the menfolk to relax a little. Collip made the first move.

'Yes please, Stella. Not too strong and no milk.'

At last, friendly chatter started, but Macleod had not quite finished. 'Gentlemen! Another matter before we break up.'

The chairs were reoccupied and silence fell.

'I think we should apply a different name to the serum. The research started with, really, only two active members: Doctor Banting and Charles Best. I am not in a position to attend your experiments, although I have given written advice on its progress – and you were quite entitled to give a name to the result of your efforts.

'I've never been entirely happy with "Isletin". Now that our team numbers four, and we have all played important parts in the project, let's try a name with which we all agree. Would anybody care to nominate one? Paulesco, the Romanian, is calling his "Pancreine" and Zuelzer, the German, terms his "Acomatol".'

There was a silence.

Macleod spoke again.

'How would "Insulin" do? It's pretty close to your own "Isletin", Doctor Banting, don't you think?'

Fred inclined his head and looked over to Charley Best, who nodded.

From that point in time, Insulin became the name applied to the extract that was to save the lives of millions, although there were to be further problems still to come.

* * *

January the 24th was a very important date for Leonard Thompson. He was, by then, unconscious most of the time. Each time his parents visited, they bid him farewell, feeling that it might be for the last time, but he hung on.

On that day, the Sister came into the ward with Walter Campbell. A nurse was carrying a tray with a hypodermic syringe, a phial of pale liquid, and a bottle of ether. Leonard did not see the doctor draw up Collip's Insulin in the syringe while the nurse drew back the bedclothes.

'Turn the boy over, nurse, please.'

It was not hard to do. The patient's last weight was down to sixty pounds.

Cleansing the skin with the ether on a swab, Campbell pushed the lengthy needle into what pathetically little flesh was left on his patient's buttock, depressed the plunger, withdrew the needle, and swabbed the site. Leonard gave no sign that he had felt anything at all.

History was made that day. The group around Leonard Thompson's bed did not think about it that way at the time, but while Banting's 'Isletin' might have worked, given a longer period of treatment, the refined 'Insulin' was certainly effective, and that within hours.

The nurse made the boy comfortable and tucked the sheets in neatly. Later in the day, another injection was given, but already the line on his blood sugar chart showed a steep downward curve, almost to normal.

'Have the boy's sugar levels checked every two hours, Sister. I think you should send someone over to the Insulin team's rooms and tell them about this, and if Professor Macleod is available, ask him to come over too, please. Take a copy of the patient's chart readings and leave them for the team to see.'

From that day, and once the press got hold of the story, the diabetic ward became a kind of Mecca for students, doctors, specialists and reporters; and diabetics, their attendants, and relatives of the other patients in the ward.

An order was introduced that only authorised persons were to be allowed admission. It proved extremely difficult to enforce.

Leonard had a good night, waking fully conscious and talking clearly. Walter Campbell examined him before giving the next injection, and this time, Leonard felt it. The doctor decided not to tell him at this stage that the injections would have to go on for the rest of his life.

'How're you feeling this morning?' Campbell asked, unbuttoning the boy's pyjama jacket and pressing a stethoscope sensor against his chest.

'A lot better, thanks. I've had some breakfast too – and enjoyed it.'

The bearer bringing the notes from the ward met Collip in the corridor, let him read them, and explained how rapid the boy's progress had been.

When the messenger left, he went straight over to the lab to find Banting was absent, and had not returned for some days.

Charley told him, 'I think he's taking a break to go to London and see his fiancée there.'

He did not, in fact, know where he was.

He was plainly delighted at the news, but worried about how he was going to tell Fred. It was going to be difficult, but their own position was encouraging. Marjorie was still doing well on her injections.

Soon after, Fred appeared. Sitting down on a stool, he took off his jacket and lit the inevitable cigarette.

'Hello there, Fred. How are you doing?'

Fred looked glum and shook his head. 'What about here? Anything exciting happened?'

It was a fair lead-in for Charley. 'Well… Yes. This'll interest you; it was handed over from the diabetic ward just a few minutes before you arrived.' He handed the carbon-copied sheets over to Banting.

Taking them over to the desk, he sat down and began to study them.

He did not detonate with anger as Charley had expected. The cigarette was stubbed out on the ashtray as he swivelled round to face his assistant.

'Come up to the roof. I'd like to have a serious talk about how we can deal with this. Bring Marjorie with you.' While Charlie went to fetch the dog, Fred found the little red ball that all the dogs played with when taken for exercise. Always ready for fun, the dog chased after the ball and dutifully fetched it back.

Fred leaned back against the parapet.

'Look here, Charley, we each signed a document agreeing to consult each other at every stage in the research. Did you have any word that this Insulin trial was to be carried out?'

Charley shook his head.

'You weren't away anywhere while I wasn't here last week and might have missed it?'

Again came a shake of the head.

'Our Marjorie has outlived any other trial. Her treatment started in November, and this is now mid-January – over seventy days. The way to prove that we were the first to find an effective extract is to put Marjorie down, have a full autopsy carried out, and present the report to Macleod. He can't argue against that.'

The dog dropped the ball at their feet and looked up at them, waiting for one of them to pick it up again. Fred threw it this time, watched the dog seize it and start on the return journey.

He continued.

'I'll have to do something. My salary stops along with the post with Velyian Henderson in a few weeks. I'll be back where I started, with no guaranteed income except my army pension, and that's pea-nuts. James Collip and the prof are passing us by and claiming the success is all theirs. They haven't treated us decently by starting Leonard Thompson off on Collip's extract like this. If all goes well, Marjorie is proof positive that *we* were there first.'

On 27 January, Charley dropped some ether on a mask and put it over the dog's head. He waited as her breathing became shallower and shallower. Soon after, Charley said quietly, 'She's away, Fred.'

Neither of them could say a word after that.

Her blanket was put over the still figure. Later in the day, they took the body over to the hospital, where a pathologist had agreed to carry out the post-mortem.

He came over a day later to give them his report.

'There was a tiny fragment of the pancreas left at the point where it should have been totally removed. While completely inert, it was enough to invalidate the claim that the animal had been rendered completely diabetic.'

It was Towser all over again.

CHAPTER 14

February 1922

The situation in the hospital ward had altered dramatically. There were six other patients with diabetes apart from Leonard Thompson. All had been making dramatic progress on Collip's insulin. Their diets on admission were so low in carbohydrate that they had been almost starving. Each was delighted by the new, body-building foods they were now given. Each time the scales were brought, a steady increase in weight was recorded. Up, dressed, and moving about, they could scarcely believe the recovery from what was, at the time of their admission to the ward, a fatal disease.

But, one day in the middle of the month, disaster struck.

The nurse doing urine tests at midday was noting the sugar levels on the charts hanging at each bed. Every patient was showing an increase, so steep that the ward sister fetched Doctor Campbell. His expression grew serious as each page was studied. Every one showed a graph climbing steeply.

'Give each of them a further injection, Sister. Fifty units each meantime. The new system for testing blood is much quicker, so I'll do this myself every hour because it's much more accurate. Oh, and tell the dieticians about this. Ask them to work out a low carbohydrate intake again for the present. I'll go over to the research team and see if they have any ideas…'

The Insulin injections were doubled, then trebled, using up every drop of the extract coming over from Collip's laboratory every two or three days, but it was no use. The patients lost colour, energy and weight, and became desperately thirsty – a sure sign that their diabetes was spiralling out of control. Within a few days, Leonard Thompson was back in bed. None of the steps the doctors and dieticians made helped him, or any of the others.

Doctor Campbell's face took on a fixed, grim expression. He knew that only the research team could solve the problem. Professor Macleod was equally worried because the press was behaving exactly as he feared they would.

Stella brought the morning papers to Macleod's desk. Fred Greenaway had managed to interview Fred Banting and Best together, after which the *Toronto Star* published an article in March:

TORONTO DOCTORS ON TRACK OF DIABETES CURE

Stella had already seen it, and watched the professor with concern as he studied the item on the front page. He folded it and put it down. Fumbling for the pipe always kept in his top pocket, filling it with tobacco, but leaving it unlit, he used it as a pointer to emphasise his remarks.

'You know, Stella, this is bad. I told the team not to talk to the press, yet look at that headline. We'll be submerged with frantic people looking for a cure. We're all aware that Insulin is *not* a cure. It can, and will, let people who would otherwise waste away and die pick up their lives again, indeed probably be more completely well than they have been for years, but we're not at the stage of releasing Insulin yet – look at what's just happened. How would the world view Toronto University if our product had been made available in every country? Just think of it.'

Lighting a match, the contents of the briar glowed red as he sucked the flame down. The tobacco smoke rose thickly above the desk.

'Get me the editor of the *Star* on the phone, would you, Stella?'

His conversation with the editor brought little consolation, although he made sure that the word 'cure' would not appear again.

'Give our extract the right name – Insulin – and call it a treatment by injection to alleviate the symptoms of diabetes.'

When he hooked the earpiece down on the pedestal, he felt

totally unconvinced that the pressman would stick to a word of his promise.

* * *

Fred could not bring himself to go back to the hospital. Staying alone in his untidy rooms made his fury about the disastrous situation mount higher and higher. Alcohol gave him relief, so he drank a lot of it.

On the fifth day, there came a knock at his door. It was Charley.

Fred looked terrible. Once inside, Charley found the stench of the unventilated room was even worse than the early days in the lab at the university.

A half-empty whisky bottle stood on the table, along with dirty cups and plates. An ashtray overflowed onto the table. Fred had not shaved for days, and looked rough. The tufty makings of a beard did nothing to enhance his appearance.

'Fred! What *are* you doing to yourself? I've waited for days, but you never came. What's wrong?' Charley opened.

His associate stared at him through red-rimmed eyes.

'What is there to come back for? I can't contribute anything now. I've decided to leave. I'll start investigating something I've been thinking about for a while – cancer. Anyway, since you and Macleod got so pally, there's been no hope for me. I'm an also-ran these days.'

The young man came forward and sat down close to where Fred was slouched on the bed.

'Listen, Fred, and listen hard. Collip's Insulin has failed. The patients that were being treated are losing the control his Insulin was having over their diabetes. You remember this happened before, when he was so sure that he'd found his extract working so well with his rabbits? Remember what he said at the lunch table? Well it's happened again, only this time with the patients at the hospital.

The professor, Collip, and a number of others are all working frantically to try to recover his formula, because once again he hasn't kept a record. It's you they need. As for leaving, if you go, I go. Come back, Fred. You were the man with the ideas. Come back and do it again. We need you. People are going to die if you don't.'

Fred sat up and looked Charley directly in the face for the first time since his visitor had arrived.

'Are you serious?'

Charley nodded.

'Of course I am. You know me better than to joke about a thing like this.'

'If that's the case, I'll come back.'

Raising the almost empty glass, he drank what was left.

'D'you see this glass? It's empty and that's the last drink I'll have until we're back on track. Go on back to the lab. I'm in a bit of a mess. I'll take a bath and get cleaned up. I'll see you there in a little while.'

'Right, Fred. You'd better shave too, I think.'

When Fred opened the door to the lab, Professor Macleod, Best and Collip, and some others were all working at the benches. Although stern-faced, they turned and even smiled a little as he stepped forward.

Fred's lab coat was still hanging from its hook. He shrugged it on. There was hardly enough room for him but they shuffled along and made space.

Lying open on the desk was James Collip's notebook. Fred slipped off the bench stool and picked it up. The last entry read 'Great difficulties were encountered chiefly because time and temperatures which were adhered to in the original method could not be obtained in a large scale process with the facilities at hand.'

There was a silence as he closed it and slammed it down on the desktop.

'This is nonsense, James. Charley and I had perfectly good results using the same 'facilities' as you refer to here. You refined our extract and claimed that you'd succeeded where we'd failed. You've failed again by not recording how you did it!'

James Collip's face paled. Professor Macleod intervened.

'Now look here... I talked to you all before about this attitude of not working together, and making unjustified comments. If you'd followed my advice, this would probably never have happened. We *must* get Insulin sorted out as a first priority. Remember the patients over in the hospital. Doctor Campbell told me this morning that one has lapsed into a coma. He doesn't hold out much hope for him unless we recover the formula. Can we try to forget these animosities just now, and get on with saving lives? Come over here, Doctor Banting, and I'll explain what we've been doing before you came in – and may I say how glad I am that you have done so.'

Fred buttoned up his coat and took the seat next to the professor.

'Well... I suppose you're right. We'd best get down to it.'

Doctor Graham appeared one morning while the group was still working together at the lab.

'Ah, Professor, I was told you were here. Can I have a word with you?'

Macleod looked up from the solution he was mixing.

'Of course! Mister Best, would you put this over the Bunsen burner and keep an eye on it? I want the liquid to evaporate 50 per cent – the mark's on the side – but don't let it boil.' He and Campbell walked outside into the corridor. The doctor had bad news.

'The patient who was so poorly has died. She was showing massively high blood sugars, and all the others have relapsed too. How are your investigations doing?'

Macleod took a few moments to reply, considering the answer carefully.

'I have to be honest, Walter. We're trying every way to retrieve

Collip's formula, but without much success so far. The reason that the Insulin failure took place was, I believe, when the manufacture of it in bulk started. The equipment to do it was set up in the basement of the medical building here by Connaught Antitoxin Laboratories, who financed it and will distribute Insulin once we can be sure of its reliability. You'll appreciate that we're all anxious to see that happen, quite apart from the serious situation with the patients.'

'I understand, but I've had to send Leonard Thomson home, along with a couple of others, as there's no Insulin left to give them. They're all back on what's still called

"Allen's Starvation Diet", and they *all* hate it – it's a severe regime. They feel we've failed them after allowing them such a generous amount of food. I feel sure you'll succeed again, but, God willing, make it soon!'

Macleod turned back into the room.

Working so close to the others, he was able to assess their abilities and deficiencies much more accurately. Banting was open, artless and lacking in tact, easily offended and quick tempered, but likeable and companionable, though the rancour towards James Collip was plain to see. Young Best was much more skilled in the scientific aspect of the research, but it was obvious that neither had much in-depth knowledge of diabetes.

Banting had been able to prove that his 'idea' worked, but had taken a wrong turning in his method of producing an effective extract.

Collip had definitely been able to produce a successful Insulin working alone and using his skill in laboratory procedures, but studying their notes in the lab desk, essential records such as ketone and blood sugar figures, weight gains and losses and, even more essentially, post-mortems, were missing.

Collip's reputation was of a slap-happy-rapid-fire experimenter, and here too, few notes had been made – the present disaster totally because of this.

The professor realised that luck had played a large part in the results from all three. It was a matter of methodical, plodding work to succeed again – and that was just what the enlarged team was now doing, though progress was agonisingly slow.

One day, Fred came out with another 'idea'.

'Look, Charley, the professor keeps nagging on about using alcohol as the initial suspension, and evaporating it to make the Insulin more potent. Well, it worked before – it's just a matter of temperature and amounts being evaporated. Why don't we speed things up a bit by using that old fan we found in the store room? It's much bigger than the thing we used before.'

They were on their own that day. Charley went off and returned with the ancient, dust-covered fan. Plugging it into a power point, the blades turned slowly at first, then gathered speed noisily. There was quite a lot of sparking from its motor as this took place.

'That's fine, Charley. See if you can find that porter – he used to be a joiner – the one who put some shelves up here for us. We need to make a wooden tunnel, where the fan can play over the trays of liquid. He'd be just the man.'

While the young assistant was away, Banting erected a bench in another unused room along the corridor. By the next day, a clumsy but operational contraption was ready, complete with warm water tubes mounted inside the open-ended tunnel and above the trays of alcohol.

The fan motor growled irregularly as it started up. Fred stood at the end of the tunnel, feeling the warm draught passing through it build up. By moving the fan farther away, they were able to control the temperature, which they decided should be 35 degrees centigrade. After a few more adjustments he stood back, satisfied.

The results were startlingly successful. Using Collip's method of 'trapping' the active extract in various percentages of alcohol, a quantity of 500cc was reduced to 50 after an hour in their contrivance.

The two men were back in their lab, when Peter Moloney, one of the assistants from another department, called.

'Is something happening?' he enquired. It was obvious from the excited expressions of the two researchers that something *was* happening.

'And what's that smell? It's alcohol, isn't it?'

The heavy odour was penetrating the entire corridor from one end to the other.

'Hi, Peter. Come along and take a look at what we're doing,' Fred invited, leading the way to the room where the noise from the fan could be heard from some distance.

'How about that, then!' Fred could hardly contain himself. 'That'll speed things along a bit, don't you think?'

Moloney was horrified. With one movement he switched the fan off and turned to Fred. 'Do you realise the danger you're in? One spark from that fan will ignite that alcohol you've got in the trays, and we'll all be blown to pieces. *And* you've got drums of the stuff in the same room as well! Fred, you mustn't run that thing a second longer.'

Angrily, Fred made to start the motor up again, but Moloney put a hand on his arm.

'Don't do it, Fred. It's a splendid idea but it's too risky that way. Just think. There was an explosion at a garage near where you live because a mechanic was smoking near some spilled gasoline. He was killed, don't you remember? And the workshop was reduced to rubble.'

Fred did remember. Stepping away from the switch, he relaxed visibly.

'I'm sorry, Peter. I just wasn't thinking. Of course you're right. I'll see the professor, and get Connaughts' men to assemble something a bit safer.'

Macleod *was* impressed, but also amazed that the apparatus had not caused a massive detonation. The attempts to succeed in tracking the formula to make Insulin once more, pressed on with added vigour. It was a dramatic event when the team managed it a few weeks later.

The Grim Reaper was kept from adding more patients to his list after treatment began again on 22 February.

Insulin injections were resumed on Leonard Thompson and the others; every day brought improvement again in weight and strength to the frail sufferers.

The next hurdle was the improvement of the small amounts of rather impure Insulin available from the laboratories and finally, to produce it in bulk. Thousands were being kept alive on a miserable diet, some barely so, waiting desperately for the lifesaving serum to become available. For some it was already too late.

Last, and certainly not least, was the part Doctor Frederick Grant Banting was to play in the Insulin distribution when it became available in quantity.

CHAPTER 15

May 1922

The conference.

Professor Macleod had been dealing solely with the immediate need to rediscover the formula for insulin. The heavy workload of administration, lectures, attendance at conferences, writing up data and dealing with vast amounts of correspondence had been set aside while he joined the others in the laboratory.

Another problem that faced him was the increasing presence of the press.

It was with mounting difficulty that he managed to keep the more intrusive reporters at bay, to stop them seeking out members of the team and holding interviews with them on their own. There were others who had joined the original group from elsewhere in the university. Velyian Henderson, the older professor (who was proving a loyal supporter of Banting in his claim to be the originator of insulin) and J.G. Fitzgerald, the director of Connaught Laboratories, were only two additional researchers; even more were working under their supervision. All these people were targets for the newsmen, and this made it impossible to keep developments under wraps. Inaccurate and excited comments made by patients and relatives, who were flattered to see their names quoted in a newspaper, added to the confusion. It was impossible to suppress such dramatic events much longer, especially when some journalists kept calling Insulin a 'cure'.

Professor Macleod called a conference in his office early in April. The company was considerably bigger than the last meeting over the creation of the name 'Insulin'.

Present were Banting, Best, Collip, Campbell, Fletcher and

Noble. The last was the fellow student of Best's who missed the opportunity of joining Banting on the turn of a coin. All had been helping to recover the formula, but in spite of the major achievement, the atmosphere towards Collip by Banting and Best remained cold. Stella appeared with her coffee jug and a tray of cups, saucers and biscuits. Nobody moved until Macleod poured out a cup for himself.

One by one, the others followed suit. As had happened before, the strained atmosphere calmed, and the professor was able to start the discussion.

'Gentlemen, you will be aware of the wildly inaccurate statements being made by many newspapers throughout Canada, America and Great Britain.

'I've called you all together as I think the time has now come to ensure that Canada is recognised – and Toronto in particular – as the place where Insulin was first discovered. It is vital that this is done soon, and it is my intention to present a paper to the Association of American Physicians in Washington on the third of May. I would like you all to participate in its composition in order that I can give a balanced report at that meeting. The presentation must be made by myself, as I am the only member of the Association in the team and I am, after all, head of the Physiology Department.

'I expect co-operation between each of you to this end. I also intend to take out a patent for Insulin under the names of Doctor Banting and Charles Best, assign it to Connaught Laboratories and the University of Toronto for its administration, and after that, set up a contract with Elli Lilly. I have had preliminary meetings with their director, George Clowes, and I am certain that they are the best people to develop Insulin to a stage of quality suitable for bulk production. Their laboratories in Indiana are amongst the finest in America. I would like you, Doctor Banting, Mister Best and Professor Collip, and any others here who would like to be present, to accompany me to Washington.'

There was an ominous silence for a few seconds, then Collip spoke.

'I'm sorry, but I'll be back in Alberta University by then: my sabbatical with you here will have run out. There's a deal of work been piling up back there, so I regret that I can't be with you.'

Fred Banting had been having a whispered conversation with Best, and stood up. Macleod wondered what was coming. Gathering some papers under his arm, he spoke coldly, without expression.

'We can't afford the trip: the hotels are expensive at these affairs. I'll submit my written version of the Insulin business in good time for you. Thank you for the invitation.'

With that, the two walked out of the room.

Macleod considered for a moment whether or not he should insist that two of the prime individuals concerned with the whole development should be present, but they were out of earshot before he could recall them.

The Washington conference was an epoch-making event. The presentation by Professor Macleod began with Banting's 'idea', right through to the discovery of an effective treatment.

Many of the eminent physicians listening to him hailed it as a world-shaking discovery. It certainly was, but thanks to the way newsmen interpreted the professor's speech and the opinions of several important members of the medical elite, the press again produced features hailing Banting (and to a lesser degree Best) as the heroes who had brought about the wonder drug. About Collip and Macleod himself there was very little.

Almost all Canadians who had anything to do with diabetes, either as physicians, patients or relatives, came to believe that this tremendously important discovery was due almost entirely to the efforts of only two people. Several newspapers splashed banner headlines across their front pages:

BANTING AND BEST: DIABETES SOLVED

There was a number of people who felt that Fred Banting had been pushed away from the credit he deserved, including some who disliked Professor Macleod and hardly knew James Collip – perhaps not surprising in the rarified atmosphere of a university.

There was Banting's cousin and boyhood friend Fred Hipwell, now a respected Toronto physician. Another was Professor Velyien Henderson, in whose department Macleod had been placed as a lecturer in title only. Also C.L. Starr, the surgeon in charge of the Christie Street Military Hospital, where Banting had worked before and after his army days – a man always ready to give help and advice when things did not go well for the young captain.

Then there was the head of the Connaught Laboratories, Professor Fitzgerald, who was disturbed when rumours got to him that it was his department that was responsible for producing faulted Insulin. Charles Collip was supposed to be with him, attempting to correct the problem, but actually spending little time at the plant.

He was working night and day with Macleod and the others upstairs in the laboratory. Fitzgerald also thought that Fred Banting was responsible for Insulin's arrival in the first place and therefore, the most likely man to recover the elusive formula.

The snag was that they were still unwilling to work together. The result of this was that Collip built up a supply of his own Insulin, and Banting and Best had theirs. Young Best promoted the view that Banting should have control over where *their* Insulin should go. Attempts to reach a fair distribution of the limited amounts failed. Independently of the others, Collip gave a quantity to Walter Campbell for the patients in his ward at Toronto General. Campbell then readmitted those who had been discharged, and Leonard Thompson resumed treatment. There was no consultation with the professor at that time.

* * *

Banting's prominence in the entire affair having leapt to the forefront due to the press, he took Charley, his fiancée Margaret Mahon, and Edith Roach out to dinner one evening by way of a celebration.

At the coffee stage, the men lit good quality cigars and Fred began to speak, cutting through the small talk.

'Now then,' he began, 'I've made a decision that you'll like to hear, Edith. I'm going to open a practice in Bloor Street, in town. That'll give me access to the hospital to treat private patients there. I've also had a visit from the Soldiers Re-establishment Department. They're going to offer facilities and let me treat patients at the Christie Street Military Hospital, where I'll be in charge of a special diabetes clinic still to be set up.'

His face flushed with delight and enthusiasm at the prospect.

'Couldn't have come at a better time,' he continued. 'My post with Professor Henderson finishes at the end of the month and so will the salary, but at last I can look forward to a decent income from the Military Hospital, and there are always people who want private treatment. There'll be plenty of diabetic ones to treat at Bloor Street, I can tell you.'

He took a gulp of wine but didn't notice the stunned expression of the others round the table before starting up again.

'We'll get married, Edith,' he blundered on. 'I can't tell you how much I've wanted to ask you – and for so long, but now I can.'

He looked fondly at her, but she did not meet his eyes. Head down, she sat expressionless, pushing the sugar spoon back and forth, rearranging over and over the grains in the bowl.

The four finished the evening with a visit to the speakeasy, where Edith was the only one sober when they left. After taking the others into town, she set off alone to drive to her parent's home. She had some serious thinking to do.

Fred was carrying furniture into the new Bloor Street surgery, when the pedestal phone rang. The operator told him to hold; there was a call from Rochester, New York State on Lake Ontario. He put the instrument to his ear and drew the speaker nearer.

'Hello. Who's speaking?'

'This is Doctor John R. Williamson. Is that Doctor Banting? Can yuh hear me OK?'

Fred asked what he could do for him.

'Ah've got a patient dying in hospital here. He's James Havens, son of the vice-chairman of Eastman-Kodak. The boy's got advanced diabetes, wasting away and not likely to have long to go – he's in a coma. Ah believe you could save him with this Insulin treatment, but we'd need it fast. If you need funding, then Haven's your man – he'll pay anything to save his son. Name any figure you want. Can yuh help?'

'I'll send a supply over today,' was the prompt answer. 'The only condition is that you keep quiet about it. We've barely enough to keep our own patients going, but I can spare a little.Thing is, I can't have a flood of diabetics coming here if word gets out.'

Doctor Williamson agreed, Banting kept his word, and James Havens began to recover. He was the first American to be treated with Insulin.

* * *

Professor Macleod was able to take up his work again, but every day Stella brought him piles of letters from hundreds of doctors, specialists and people with diabetes, many seriously ill, all pleading to know when the wonder drug would be available.

After a few days of attempting to deal with this, Macleod took the bundle through to his secretary and dumped it on her desk.

'Doctor Banting seems to have appointed himself head cook and bottle washer as regards the distribution of Insulin business. Have a messenger take each day's mail down to his surgery, and ask him to deal with it.'

Looking up at him, Stella thought she saw a glimmer of a smile.

The reason that Banting had sufficient Insulin to treat young Havens was an agreement reached with Professor Fitzgerald soon after the 'new' formula had been achieved. Once Connaught got hold of it, production in gradually increasing amounts began.

Fitzgerald arranged for two thirds of the Insulin to be allocated to Doctor Banting. The rest went to Walter Campbell to treat the patients in his ward.

A few days before departing to start up his new surgery at Bloor Street, Banting had a caller. He was alone; Charles Best had been appointed to supervise production of Insulin in bulk down at the Connaught laboratories. The caller was George Eastman of Eastman-Kodak. Fred offered him a seat and once the introductions were complete, Eastman came straight to the point.

'I can offer you a post at our new medical school at Rochester. I'm on the board of directors, and I'm authorised to offer you a good salary if you'll accept.'

The figure he named was a fortune.

Banting considered the proposition. He was still angry and disappointed at the way Walter Campbell had behaved over the Leonard Thompson episode. Professor Macleod rated pretty low in his estimation because, in Banting's view, he and Collip were still trying to steal the credit for the discovery of Insulin. Toronto University did not seem to want him, but everybody else did.

The offer from Eastman was not the only one. Doctor Henry Kellog, the corn flakes millionaire, had said that a diabetes unit would be built at his sanatorium at Battle Creek, Michigan, with a salary of $10,000 a year for Banting.

An entry in Banting's diary described another:

'This fat man paid me a call today at my Bloor Street rooms. He had a cheque made out to me for a million dollars ready to exchange for a patent rights assignment. Told me he would arrange clinics in every big city across the United States, and I would be medical director... I told him to go away.'

The rejection of such huge rewards was an indication of Frederick Banting's determination to keep his country in the forefront as the place where the discovery of Insulin had taken place.

But there was another reason. Acceptance of any of these offers would have set him in the midst of the very medical academics in whose presence he felt so uncomfortable. Fred was not a member of that autocratic elite. Because he was not the wearer of an 'old school tie', he was not acceptable in their circles.

At Christie Street, his chief would be Clarence Starr, a man he liked. His patients would be soldiers of the type he knew so well: men who spoke his kind of language, smoked cigarettes, swore steadily, and told bawdy jokes.

At Bloor Street, Frederick Banting's brass plate would be on the door. *He* would be in charge, *he* would make the decisions, and *he* would take the rap if things went wrong.

Taking a cigarette box from the desk, he proffered it to Eastman, who shook his head. He lit one himself and drew deeply on it.

'Your proposition is tempting, to say the least, but I have to tell you that I have already accepted another post.'

George Eastman tried for a little longer, but recognised that Banting's resolve was final, rose to his feet, and held out his hand.

'I know that my fellow directors will be sad when I tell them that you are not able to join us, but I know I speak for them when I wish you the best of luck with your remarkable discovery.'

* * *

Fred was immersed in the hustle of starting off his new practice, but in the evening, alone in the quiet rooms, his mind turned again to Edith Roach.

One Friday evening, thinking back on their dinner out together, he recollected how silently she had reacted to his remark: 'now we can get married'.

He reached for the telephone and asked the operator to connect him with her home. She spent most weekends there, and answered his call.

'Edith, darling. How are you?'

She replied that her week at the school had been busy. Similar pleasantries followed, but none of the usual working round to the marriage question rose from her. Fred sensed that there were problems.

'Why not come over to Toronto?' Fred asked. 'My cousin Fred Hipwell and his wife'll put you up, like they've done before. We could take the weekend off for a rest, and I'll be able to let you see my brand-new surgery. Something you always wanted me to do – start a general practice again.'

'Well… all right. I *am* glad to hear you're ready to start up again, and I'm sure it'll be much more successful than your first attempt. I'll see you later tomorrow morning then.'

As she stepped from the car at Bloor Street, Fred was waiting at the door. He pointed out the brass plate on the doorjamb with his name neatly engraved on it.

He had kept it since the failure of the practice in London. They hugged, and he took her hand as they went inside. There was the welcoming smell of coffee from a jug simmering on a cooker in the little scullery at the back of the rooms.

Bringing through a tin tray with cups and biscuits, he set it on the desk in the consulting room.

'Well, Edith. Here we are. What do you think of the place?'

She got up and crossed to the window.

'Yes, Fred. It's nice… Big room too.' She took in the newly painted walls hung with a few watercolours.

'These are your work, aren't they? You've come a long way since the painting you gave me all these years ago.'

Fred had been keen on sketching and painting for a long time.

'I sometimes go to an artists' club near here. There's another fellow and I planning a sketching trip some time. When we've got a house of our own, I'll do some scenes to hang in our rooms there.'

Edith did not respond to the subtleties of the remark.

The rest of the weekend was spent walking in the parks and eating out. The Hipwells gave them a meal and ate with them in the evening, but left them alone for a time before Fred departed again to his rooms. It had been a pleasant enough day, but that Sunday evening did not finish up well.

Fred patted his hand on the cushions of a settee and invited his fiancée to come and sit beside him. Edith did so, but did not embrace him as in former days.

'Come on, Edith. Haven't had a decent kiss for weeks.'

Still she did not come to his arms. She was not smiling. In fact, she was obviously unhappy.

'Fred… I can't keep myself from telling you… Something I have to say.'

Fred straightened up, his expression serious. 'What's wrong? I've looked forward to saying how much I love you, how much I want you. Is there someone else?'

'No. No… There's no one else, but I can't marry you.'

There were tears in her eyes again, but she did not try to hide them, and forced herself to carry on, her voice tense with emotion.

'All these years… I tried so hard to make you see how much I wanted you for my husband. There was never anyone else. You must have seen that, but you wouldn't listen to me. I watched you get so thin, so tired, so poor, and yet, so proud. You made me angry with your pride.

'You couldn't let me share the expense of setting up a home when I was so desperate to look after that side of things, and now you're going to be rich, you expect me to trot away with you like some lovestruck teenager.'

Fred sat, numbly taking in what the girl was saying, and realising that what she was saying was all perfectly true.

'Edith…'

'No! Listen to me. Let me finish. You remember me telling you that people were beginning to say that I'd be an old maid. Well, I feel that these same people will think that I'm marrying you because you're famous now, marrying you for the money… I simply can't do it, Fred. I've matured a lot since we met.'

I've got a good job and earn good money. You made it plain that when we were married, I'd not work. Well, I enjoy my teaching and I love the children there. I know it's not the thing for the wife to work, but things have changed since the War. I'd like to think a bit longer, and you should too. You're going to be very busy for the next year or two – need all your energy dealing with all these patients. I'm not going to do anything in a hurry, Fred. We can give each other a little more time, can't we?'

Fred realised she was absolutely sincere, she meant every word; but he had been building up dreams about their being married, buying a roses-round-the-door little house with a neat garden and a patio at the back where they could sit and watch the kids on the swing…

The Hipwells appeared to have a night cap with them. They saw that something had happened but made no comment. Later, Edith gave Fred a longer hug than usual at the door as he left. She felt desperately sorry for him, yet glad that the ordeal of putting her feelings to him was over. He looked so sad that she tried to say something that would cheer him up a little.

'Don't look so depressed Fred. It's not the end of the world.

Give me a ring next week.'

Back at the lodgings, Fred sat for a long time. He knew he had lost her. A stiff whisky did not help nor did sleep draw its soothing wings around him that night.

June

It was another scorching summer, almost as hot as the record-breaking one of the preceding year. The amount of Insulin coming from Connaught Labs was still woefully limited.

There was a caller at the Bloor Street surgery one day. It was a former classmate, Joe Gilchrist.

They had not met for years, and Fred shook hands so vigorously that Joe had to restrain the welcome. It was then that Fred noticed how thin and pale his old friend looked.

'Sit down, Joe. I can't tell you how pleased I am to see you. Here, read the paper until I finish this job. It'll only take a few minutes.'

The 'job' was a wretched task. On the desk were three piles of letters. Beside them were three sets of duplicated replies, each conveying a different answer. Fred was attaching one of these to each letter. This was the day's delivery from Stella – the mail redirected from Professor Macleod's office.

Only one reply gave hope to the applicant: 'Attend the clinic at Bloor Street for further examination…'

The next was addressed to Walter Campbell at Toronto General, asking if there might be a bed available for selected patients, usually young and usually seriously ill with diabetes. The list was so long that death often forestalled the longed-for admission.

The third letter gave little hope to the applicant. 'We regret that there is no Insulin available at the present time. We cannot therefore help you. Please write to us again in two months.'

Fred hated the task. It meant that he alone had to decide who lived and who died, but there was nothing more he could do, other than curse the man who had brought this to him, J.J.R. Macleod.

Pinning the last one ready for the secretary to mail off, Fred turned back to Joe.

'Quite a write-up you keep getting, Fred,' he remarked. The newspaper he was reading had another story from a grateful relative of a recovering diabetic.

The conversation was general, until Fred suggested that they go round to a café on the corner and have lunch together. As they examined the menu, Joe poured out a glass of water and drank it almost at once, refilling it again a few minutes later.

He made a remark next that Fred found not unexpected.

'Fred, I've got diabetes. I developed it shortly after I left school, and got on fairly well staying off high carbohydrate foods and sweet drinks. I took a dose of flu last year and it seemed to trigger off a much more severe level of diabetes. I've lost a huge amount of weight, and I can't stay away from the tap more than five minutes. The amount of water I pass is abnormal. I'm a doctor myself, so I know what it's all about. Can you help me?'

Fred looked at the man opposite, noting the skin stretched tightly over prominent cheekbones and hands, the sunken eye sockets, the empty jug of water. Impulsively he reached across the table and laid a hand on Joe's.

'Of course I'll help you. Come back to the surgery right now and let's see what I can do.'

A blood test revealed a dangerously high sugar level. Fred sat down after completing it, and told Joe the result.

'I have some Insulin here, but it may be impure. I suggest we try it by mouth today. If it doesn't work, come back to Bloor Street tomorrow.'

He should have known that it would not work. Both they and other researchers had never found that Insulin taken orally had any effect whatever.

The following day, Joe was back, looking even frailer.

'Right, Joe. Roll up your sleeve and I'll give you an injection this time. Stay here until lunchtime, and we'll do another blood test.'

The result of this showed only a very slight reduction.

'I'm sorry, Joe. Look, I'll give you another injection – all the Insulin I have here, but I've got to go to Christie Street this afternoon. Here's the phone number. Give me a ring if anything happens. You can't do a blood test alone, so come back again tomorrow. I've got another idea I want to talk to you about anyway.'

Mid-afternoon, Fred was summoned to the telephone. It was Joe Gilchrist.

His voice was excited.

'Fred! You've no idea what I feel like! It all happened so suddenly! My thirst's gone, I've got energy back. Words can't describe what you've done for me. I'll see you tomorrow.'

The smile of satisfaction that crossed Fred's face as he hung the earpiece back was something he had not worn for a very long time.

Even so short a time after the first Insulin injection, Joe looked a new man. He walked upright, his eyes were bright, his manner cheerful. Without waiting to be asked, he rolled up a shirtsleeve and let Fred take blood. The test was good – the blood sugar almost normal.

'Now sit down, Joe. I need to talk about how I can continue to treat you, because the only place I can get a supply of Insulin is at the Military Hospital. I've had a word with my boss, Clarence Starr. He says I can ask you to join me as an assistant. If you're with me, you can get Insulin, and that way, we'll make you well again. I don't think the salary will be much, but I doubt if that matters a lot to you, does it?'

The look in Joe's eyes said it all. He reported for duty the very next day.

CHAPTER 16

May–December 1922

A number of events took place that brought Frederick Banting even more to the forefront.

His telephone rang constantly, adding to the demands created by answering letters, consulting patients at Bloor Street, dealing with army men at Christie Street, and private cases at Toronto General.

Charley Best met him during one of his visits to the diabetic ward, and joined him for lunch at the staff restaurant.

'Well, Fred! It's good to see you.'

They were on excellent terms, not least because Best was still supplying a greater amount of insulin to Banting than to Doctor Campbell.

'Things are a bit hectic, Charley, but we get through. I keep wishing that Lilly would increase their deliveries – I have to say that their Insulin *is* purer than yours, but then Connaught's facilities can hardly be as sophisticated as Lilly's. On a more cheerful note, I have a story to tell about one of my army patients. He had mild diabetes and was sent to Christie Street. His blood sugars were high and had been for some weeks. Impotence was worrying him. In fact, he was more concerned about that than he was about his deteriorating health. The second day I put him on Insulin, he asked for a twenty-four hour pass and he went out that night.

'On his return next morning, he came to my office, wild and flushed with excitement. He couldn't wait to tell me something. "Doctor Banting! You're a miracle worker! I went downtown to find some girls who'd look after me last night and guess what? I'd a marvellous time! Better able to please them than I'd ever been before you put me on this Insulin stuff. When can I get some more?" So you can see, Charley, how important it is that we have enough to treat not just the people at Christie Street and the hospital, but the whole of Canada and later, the world. Keep at it, Charley, keep at it.'

At the university, Charles Best had been given control of Insulin production at the Connaught Laboratories, ever since James Collip had returned to Alberta. The rooms that had been given over for the overflow of scientists trying to recover Collip's lost formula in February remained full. The scientists were working to decrease the impurities in Insulin, still causing problems with painful abscesses and swellings at the injection sites. It was the price that sufferers had to accept if they wanted to stay alive.

One of the phone calls to Banting one day was from Doctor Williams at Rochester. It was about James Haven again.

'Say, Doctor Banting, Ah've got problems. The Insulin you're sending's not doing too good. James is quite ill, showing extra-high sugar readings, an' there's ketones showing again. Can you give me any suggestions?'

Fred's heart sank. There were people in his care who were also, once more, showing the same symptoms.

'Look, Doctor, I know the difficulty. We've got the same problems here. It seems to happen every time attempts are made to produce Insulin in bigger quantities. I'm going to see Eli Lilly's lab staff in Indiana next week – they're contracted to undertake bulk supplies within a month or two. October's indicated. Is Havens so poorly that he'll not last that long? We're so short of Insulin here.'

There was a hesitation before the caller answered. 'I'm afraid so. He's unable to move from bed. He's got all the symptoms of declining control of his diabetes. You know what that means.'

Fred asked how much Insulin Williams had left.

'Only a couple of days.'

'Right. Double the dose today. I'll supply enough to last another week, and we'll see how things go. It's the best I can do at the moment.'

'There's another problem. The boy's in great pain from the injections. There's a number of sores come up and I think he needs a day or two off Insulin to allow recovery…'

'Try reducing his carbohydrate. Give him meat, beef tea, plenty of vegetables, apples and oranges while he's off the Insulin. I'll try to come and see him, but I'm submerged in work at the moment. The priority's to purify the extract more, but there's a while to go before that happens.'

Williams hung up. He did not tell Banting that his suggestions had already been tried.

Professor Macleod was uneasy about the way Banting was, in his view, commandeering the greater share of available Insulin. The situation was difficult.

Doctor Campbell, Professor of Medicine Duncan Graham, and he met to discuss the problem one morning. Graham was not a Banting supporter, and highly protective of his patients.

'I'm against using them as guinea-pigs. I'd have preferred clinical testing to wait until Insulin has been proved completely reliable. Look what happened with Banting and his Isletin in January. It failed, and my patient Leonard Thompson had to wait until Professor Collip produced an effective serum – and then *that* failed.'

He continued rather grumpily. 'We're no better than we were in January. As regards this problem of insufficient Insulin, it was said to me the other day that Campbell knows all about diabetes but can't treat it, and Banting knows nothing about diabetes and *can* treat it…'

Macleod listened carefully before speaking. 'Look, Duncan. Canada is going to lose its rightful place if what I think might happen takes place.

'According to the press, Banting and Best were the creators of Insulin. Banting has received several glowing offers from powerful

American medical institutions. He's already treating an American patient who's under the care of a Rochester doctor. If he leaves for America, the press will glorify him there, and we'll fade away.

'I can see it coming and it must not happen. Look, he's getting the use of beds here, there are more patients than he can cope with, and he'll stay in Canada meantime. To be fair, he has told me about some of the enormous offers he's had, but as long as there's a likelihood that purer Insulin will be accessible to him in bulk soon, he'll stay. I think we'll have to leave the situation as it is meantime.'

The group broke off the conversation and left soon after.

Stella was asked to contact Banting, and he arrived at the professor's office a few hours later. He apologised to Macleod for the length of time taken to answer the summons, and was invited to sit down. He watched Macleod's face closely, assuming that criticism of his activities was coming. He was right.

The professor put his papers aside, and there was the squeak of leather as he settled back to start his talk.

'I've asked you to come because of disquiet on the part of the hospital board, Professor Campbell, Doctor Graham, myself, and others responsible for the treatment of diabetics in the ward. I understand that you are receiving far more Insulin than anyone else for your private patients directly from Eli Lilly at Indiana *and* Connaught here. While we are doing our best to cope with the increasing numbers of patients needing help, your private patients and our own, we simply can't deal with things in this manner. It's not the way I expect my clinical associate to behave.'

Banting looked up sharply, having noticed the change of title. 'Clinical associate', no less. Indeed! The professor continued.

'Campbell, Graham and I have discussed this today. We wish you to send no more private patients to the hospital. The beds allocated to you are all full and secondly, we've not got enough effective Insulin to treat those who are here already. Will you agree?'

Banting nodded. 'Well, I'll try. You gave me the job of answering all the letters. It's a hell of a thing to have to do and I simply haven't the heart to say no to them all. I'm only referring the worst cases – you'll have seen them yourself. They have to be carried into the building on stretchers – and that's only the ones that I think have a chance.'

Macleod nodded sympathetically. 'Yes, I know. But hopefully supplies in sufficient quantity will be coming soon.'

A further notion had occurred to the professor, one that might make Banting more aware of the unfairness of his behaviour.

'I'm aware of attempts to wean you away from here, but you seem to be content with the positions you now hold. You mentioned some weeks ago that you would like to establish a 50 to 100 bed diabetic clinic here in Toronto, and that you could obtain $500,000 to help build it?'

Banting sat up abruptly. This was a new slant, coming from a man he considered had never helped him.

'Yes… that's right,' he replied cautiously, surprised, and waited for Macleod to carry on. His own hopes about finance were that the Eastman Corporation could be tapped, but he had said nothing to the professor about that.

'We can offer you a post with Professor Duncan Graham. Assisted by Doctors Campbell and Fletcher, you can set up a 32-bed unit at the hospital. The salary would be $6000 a year – not a lot, but all we can afford. The offer has a lot of advantages. You could still attend your Christie and Bloor Street patients because Campbell and Fletcher can look after the patients with full and absolute competence when you're not available. It answers a lot of problems. Think about it, will you, and let me know once you've decided.'

The offer of the post to Banting was accepted by Duncan Graham after long arguments, mainly based on reluctance to allow Fred Banting anywhere near any of his patients.

'Thank you, Professor. I'll be in touch.'

Banting rose. He got a handshake this time.

He was not stupid. He did not rush to accept, realising at once how the professor was hoping to solve the problem of Insulin distribution – but these were the very men who had refused him entry to treat Leonard Thompson…

The summer passed quickly. Banting was everywhere. At Christie Street in the mornings early, at Bloor Street from midday, seeing patients and attending to the pile of letters that got bigger every day. Dictating to Sadie Gair – a research assistant appointed to look after the growing amount of administrative work, was something she did very well while also becoming something of a mother figure to the sometimes-exhausted Banting.

When he did not appear at her office before she left at the end of the day, she often found him down in the basement working in the Connaught laboratory trying to solve the quality problem of Insulin. Making sure he set off for home at a reasonable time, she saw how distressed he was becoming over the lack of success.

Banting set off one day, appearing at the downtown office of the chairman of the board of governors, Sir Edmund Walker. Storming past his secretary, he confronted the surprised executive.

'Look here, Sir Edmund, we need money! You people on the board don't realise how poor Connaught's equipment to manufacture Insulin is. I need $10,000 NOW! People are dying every day because we haven't enough. What there is, is poor stuff.'

Walker stayed calm.

'We can't just produce that kind of money without going through the proper procedures. There'd need to be a board meeting first.'

'If I can get hold of it myself, will your damned board accept it? That's the question…'

By this time, Banting had his palms on the front edge of Walker's desk, his face an angry red, a foot away from Walker's.

'Look, sit down a minute. Of course we'd accept it, just like any other donation, but you'd need to get it first. Whether the board would agree to your taking charge of its use is another matter, I'm afraid.'

Banting straightened up and walked out, slamming the door behind him. Walker found himself trembling after such a furious verbal attack.

The next train to New York had Banting on board, on his way to the home of a rich diabetic man who had been treated at Toronto. He simply asked how much was to be entered on the cheque...

The next stop was at the great Doctor Frederick Allen's clinic at Morristown, New Jersey, to compare notes with him. His patients were slowly starving to death on an almost forcibly imposed low carbohydrate diet... but they were still alive, praying for Insulin to arrive.

One who was later to come to Toronto was a skeletal girl of fifteen. Her name was Elizabeth Hughes, and she was Allen's prize subject. Introduced to him, her thin hand disappeared in Banting's. The dress she was wearing hung loosely on a frail, emaciated figure. Sunken eyes gazed at him, but they were bright in spite of her fragility.

'I've heard of you,' she murmured.

Wood's Hole, Massachusetts, the headquarters of Eli Lilly, was the next stop, to confer with George Clowes, the research director heading their own efforts to bring out fully effective Insulin.

During overnight stays, several visitors at his hotels came with yet more tempting offers. All were rejected. One was of $100,000 a year for part-time attendance at a clinic in New York City. His usual charge to private patients was $100 a week, an extra $25 to be on call night and day... Much less than that if the patient could not afford to pay for his services.

Strangers liked him. Many who became friends supported him in any way they could, often publicly, in his insistence that he alone had brought Insulin into being and that Professor Macleod had done nothing to help.

* * *

August–September 1922

People who saw what happened to friends and relatives after receiving injections of Insulin were amazed. Elizabeth Hughes was not the only one having difficulty in finding words to describe the resurrection of diabetics when Insulin began, albeit slowly, to increase in purity and availability.

One was a Toronto woman, Charlotte Clarke, whose physician was Doctor L.C. Palmer, a former medical officer who had been with Fred Banting in the trenches at Cambrai in 1918. He telephoned his old friend about Mrs Clarke one day in the summer of 1922.

After exchanging news, he got to the point.

'Fred, I've a great favour to ask. I have this patient who's got a gangrenous infection in her right ankle. It's spreading up the limb, and the only way out is to amputate the leg. There's not a surgeon in Toronto who'll take her on because she's severely diabetic. They say it'd be a waste of time. The wound never heals and the infection eventually kills the patient, they say. Well, that's true enough, but I'd like to save her if I can. Insulin might help, and I want to give it a try. Can you possibly see her tomorrow? She's in a bad way.'

There was no way his former army companion could refuse.

'Of course I'll help. Bring her over as soon as you can,' Fred answered.

The request could not have come at a worse time. Insulin was in very short supply, but as soon as Charlotte Clarke arrived, it was obvious she was deeply unwell and on the brink of diabetic coma. The only way Insulin could be provided for her was to suspend treatment of other patients in the ward. An amputation below the knee was carried out successfully. Acetone and blood sugar checks every few hours for the next few days enabled Insulin injections to be given in carefully calibrated amounts, and Banting was able to report that the wound was healing normally.

It was the first operation carried out on an Insulin-dependent diabetic, and by September, she had an artificial leg fitted and was happily making her way about. The others in the ward, who had been barely surviving without Insulin, had their treatment resumed when fresh supplies arrived a few days later.

There were many recoveries similar to that, thanks to Insulin.

Others were not so fortunate. In the early attempts to produce bulk quantities, Eli Lilly used beef pancreases from the abattoirs to begin with. Later, pigs were successfully adopted, which gave a choice of Insulins – porcine or bovine – but both were still variable and erratic in strength. Some patients reacted violently to one or the other because of allergies, others died because of severe hypogly-caemic attacks – dangerously low blood sugars – just like Collip's rabbits in December 1921 and January 1922.

Paula Inge was the eleven-year-old daughter of the Dean of St Paul's Cathedral in London, England. Diabetes had been diagnosed in November 1921.

The doctors gave her three weeks to live. She was a much-loved little girl, and her parents were devastated.

In December, her father made enquiries about Insulin from Doctor Henry Dale, head of the British Medical Research Council.

Macleod had already had a letter from a Canadian doctor at Edinburgh Royal Infirmary pleading for a supply of Insulin for Scotland, which prompted him to write to the BMRC offering them complete British patent rights to the extract. Fitzgerald, Director of Toronto's Connaght Laboratories was in England within a month to discuss matters with the Council.

Their reaction was typical of official bodies – particularly British ones. The recently formed body of experts was sceptical and uncertain about what to do next. A report from their committee read

'New drugs are notified for all sorts of disease every week. The Americans are forever claiming new wonder cures for everything under the sun... How do we know this one is anything different?'

Time dragged on and Dale wrote, in answer to Paula's father, 'The serum is still in the experimental stage and not available...'

The Dean resigned himself to the inevitable. His daughter was going to die.

His reply simply said, 'God speed the Medical Council', and in 1923 she was still alive, although failing fast. She was the equivalent to Toronto's Elizabeth Hughes, but she was not to be so fortunate. By the time supplies of American Insulin began to arrive from Lilly, supplementing the small quantity being made in the UK by Burroughs Wellcome, it was too late. She fell into a coma and died on Maundy Thursday in March 1923. Supplies of Insulin began to arrive in April.

Her parents consoled themselves with the thought that God had given them a whole year's grace before taking her from them.

It was no fault of medical science. It had done all it could, but not quite quickly enough.

Frederick Banting was not the only one faced with decisions on who was to live and who to die.

One part of Europe where lack of finance was limiting the development of Insulin was Germany. The Great War had bankrupted the country, and it was reckoned that it might be 1924 or 1925 before supplies would be accessible.

One morning in 1922, Professor Minkowski, for many years a specialist in pancreatic research, was giving his regular morning lecture to students at Breslau University. Tall, distinguished, white-haired and bearded, he was greeted with the pupils stamping their feet in an enthusiastic welcome – he was a popular lecturer.

He stepped forward as the young students fell silent, and lifted a small phial from his white coat pocket.

'This, gentlemen, is the first Insulin to reach our country. Professor J.J.R. Macleod and Doctor Frederick Banting in Toronto, the discoverers, have sent it to me. It was once my hope that I might have been the "Father" of Insulin. Now I am happy to accept the designation as its grandfather, a title which the Toronto scientists have conferred on me so kindly.'

More thunderous stamping of feet followed his remarks.

The doors to the lecture hall opened, and porters brought in two trolleys. On one lay an elderly diabetic man with an ulcer on his foot. His dressings had been removed so that the students could observe the wound. The other was an obviously sick child, also suffering from diabetes, limp, pale and barely conscious. Minkowski held up the tiny phial.

'I have only enough here to treat one of these patients for a very short time. Now. To which do you think I should give it?'

The students turned to each other, but did not take long to decide.

'To the child…. It looks so ill. Surely Insulin would help recovery?'

He shook his head.

'No. It must go to the man. The child is suffering from keto-acidosis – the final stage before death – which will come within a day or so. There is not enough Insulin to treat the child in the long term. There is much more hope that the man's ulcer will heal and his diabetes be kept at bay through strict dieting until a further supply of Insulin comes, but it will take time. The physician must be realistic and use cool and prudent judgement.'

He signalled to the porters. 'Please take these patients out.'

The students were silent.

They were learning at first hand the difficulties ahead of them – difficulties that the venerable professor had illustrated so vividly.

* * *

Banting and Best revelled in the hero worship with which the media was lauding them. Charley was now in charge of the Insulin production at the Connaught laboratory, working with Fitzgerald; and although Eli Lilley had spent a huge amount of money on its efforts to produce a reliable Insulin in bulk, Banting never gave either of the laboratories any recognition for their work. He had no hesitation, however, in accepting supplies of their product for administration to his patients, both at Toronto and Christie Street Hospitals.

The press was to be the cause of severe arguments over just who discovered Insulin. Opinions were to be divided for many years.

Banting claimed that he alone had discovered the magic extract by means of his pancreatic duct ligation 'idea'. He alone had successfully treated Elizabeth Hughes, Leonard Thomson, James Havens, Charlotte Clarke, restored the sex drive to dozens of diabetic soldiers…. What more proof did anyone need?

The press boosted tales of the 'Local Farm Boy Makes Good' format. The *Toronto Star* gushed into print: 'From behind his glasses looked forth a pair of eyes which even in their most casual glance gave the impression of penetrating beneath the surface of things and reading secrets not revealed to ordinary eyes…'

Another effused: 'What visions, could one but read them, must lie behind the quiet, dreaming eyes of that inscrutable face?'

If Collip and Macleod had been asked, they might have told an entirely different story.

The welter of misinformation from the media continued to infuriate Banting and Macleod, to say nothing of confusing the public.

A feature that appeared in the *Toronto Star* lit the blue touch paper yet again to Banting's quick temper. It set off the biggest explosion up to that point in the relationship between Macleod and Banting.

The press item referred to Insulin, and the attention it was receiving abroad.

Part of it included a letter by Professor Sir William Bayliss of University College, London, which had appeared in *The Times*.

It stated that Professor Macleod was getting inadequate credit for the Insulin discovery, and that Banting was 'one of the collaborators who had helped in the clinical application'. It continued, 'The discovery is the result of the painstaking and lengthy investigations of Professor Macleod, which have extended over many years, and it is to *him* that the chief credit should be given.'

Bayliss was quite incorrect, but the article was taken at once by an irate Fred Banting for a confrontation with the professor the day the newspaper reached the streets.

Stella had just arrived for her work when he stormed into Macleod's office.

He emerged, hot and red-faced soon after, still carrying a copy of the newspaper. Stella paused at her typewriting to greet him, but thought better of it when she saw his expression. The rate he stalked past her would not have allowed time for any sort of salutation in any case.

The professor had asked her to take dictation just before Banting arrived without an appointment, so she picked up her pad, tapped on the door and walked in.

Macleod was frowning, silent, brooding. He pointed to the chair.

'Stella, I'm deeply concerned. You know what difficulties Doctor Banting has caused me, and most of the hospital staff. He's causing even more trouble this time.'

Stella put the pad on the desk and waited. It was plain that her boss wanted a sympathetic ear.

'He's furious about this article in the *Star*. I told him I'd nothing to do with it, but he knows Bayliss is a friend of mine, and thinks I put him up to it. He's still obsessed with the notion that I'm trying to steal his thunder. Wants me to send word to the press that he's the one – he alone, and nobody else, invented Insulin. Acceptance of such an arrogant suggestion is out of the question.

'I told him I'd send an article to the *Star* clarifying the whole thing, and this needs to be done at once. Take this down, and I'll sign it after you've typed it up. I'd like it delivered by hand today, please.'

Stella took up her pad and Macleod began…

'With regard to the letter which appeared recently in *The Times*, Sir William Bayliss is wrong in stating that the idea of preparing Insulin from the pancreas some time after ligaturing the ducts originated with me.

'This is particularly the work that originated with Dr Banting, who, in collaboration with Mr Best, put it to experimental test in my laboratories.

'As a result of successful demonstration of the effects on animals of extracts from this source, the problem of the physiological action of Insulin was then taken up by the Physiological Department of the university by a group of workers including Dr Banting and Mr Best, and under my direction.'

The professor reached for his pipe.

'Now read that back. Tell me if you think that it gives accurate credit to Banting – and Best – for the part they played in this discovery.'

A few minutes later, Stella left her desk with the signed article, heading for the *Toronto Star* offices.

Fred Banting called down at the Connaught laboratory and asked Charles Best to come up to his office. Charley guessed what was coming. He had seen the article in the *Star*.

'Sit down and listen to me,' Fred began.

Charley interrupted.

'Save your breath. I've seen the *Star* feature. I think we've been badly treated. I'm not even named, let alone Collip and all the others who were in the team.'

He looked briefly at Fred. His senior was visibly shaking, his voice hoarse and strained. Flinging the paper down on the bench, Fred smacked his palm on it so hard that the retorts in their racks rattled and clinked against each other.

'Look, this man Macleod.... He's never to be trusted. He is the most selfish man I have ever known. He has sought at every possible opportunity to advance himself. If you tell anything to Macleod in the morning, it'll be in print or in a lecture by the evening. He is grasping, selfish, deceptive, self-seeking and empty of truth, yet he is clever as a speaker and writer. He never produced a physiologist, for he took all that anyone had for his own purpose. He loves acclaim and applause. He has a selfish, overpowering ambition. He is unscrupulous, and would steal an idea or credit for work from any possible source. Like all bullies, Macleod is a coward and a skulking weakling if things don't go his way!'

(Based on Banting's 1940 accounts of the discovery of Insulin.)

Charley could find no answer to the torrent of invective. Never before, during any of the times when Fred had lost his temper, had he heard such an outpouring of venom.

He sat quietly, waiting. It was the best policy as Fred continued to express even more fiercely his feelings towards his mentor.

Eventually he pulled a bottle from the cupboard under his desk, and poured stiff whiskies into two glasses.

'Take a drink, Charley. I'll see that little swine off yet. Just see if I don't!'

The evening edition of the *Toronto Star*, in the most appalling editing of the professor's carefully prepared piece, printed this:

GIVES DOCTOR BANTING CREDIT FOR INSULIN

'The credit for the complete discovery of Insulin extract for the treatment of diabetes was given today to Doctor F.G. Banting by Professor J.J.R. Macleod.

This is an important statement. It once and for all authoritatively refutes the imputation in the London Times and some American papers that it was improbable that so young and comparatively inexperienced a laboratory man as Doctor Banting himself could have made this epoch making discovery in the history of medicine.'

The last few weeks of 1922 passed. Banting had no contact with the professor again until it was absolutely imperative; he was busy enough with his patients, but wanted to advance his researches into further improvements in Insulin. He also told several friends that, fed up with the situation about insulin, he had some more 'ideas' about a cure for cancer.

More laboratory space was needed, so an appointment was made to see Macleod about this. Stella gave him her usual smile.

'Just go in, Doctor. He's expecting you.' The professor sat back as Banting appeared. He was not invited to sit down.

'Good morning. What can I do for you?' asked Macleod.

Banting wasted no time.

'I need less criticism from Duncan Graham. He's never seen eye to eye with me about anything, and I object to such an attitude.'

Macleod stared at him and laid down the pen he had been using before replying.

'Walter Graham is one of our most expert specialists. He founded the diabetic clinic over in the hospital and has looked after it for years. In what way does he criticize?'

'He doesn't believe his patients should be allowed to eat what they want, but I say they should. By calibrating their Insulin to correspond with their carbohydrate intake, lost weight is recovered quickly.

He has contradicted me several times, even in front of other staff.'

Banting talked on, seemingly forgetting that his lecture was being delivered to a man whose expertise in carbohydrate metabolism was respected throughout the western world.

'Elizabeth Hughes is a good example of a patient who benefited fast by giving her large amounts of food, as and when she wanted it. Graham was very upset about that until I proved him wrong.'

Banting did not tell him that Graham and he had almost come to blows on some occasions. Their relationship had never been good, and Banting had never forgiven him for not proceeding with *his* Insulin in the case of Leonard Thompson.

Banting's theory about dietary freedom was strong, one which was certain to prove controversial when the experts firmly believed that strict dieting was absolutely necessary. Some agreed with Banting, others did not.

In fact, both views were right; some diabetics could tolerate more carbohydrate than others.

The professor waited, making no comment. He sensed there was more to come.

'I need more lab space. You may remember that when we were all working to sort out Collip's silly mistake, I was forced to give up the rooms. Well, now I need them back.'

Macleod tried to control his response to Banting's aggressive choice of words, but the situation put to him was fair. He had foreseen that Banting's demand would be on the agenda, and had discussed the matter with Velyien Henderson in expectation of it.

'That's all been put in hand, Doctor. There'll be a couple of lab rooms made available for you by Professor Henderson in his pharmacology department. Will that suit you?'

Banting scowled at him, surprised and disappointed at having his thunder stolen.

'Yes, well… I suppose so.'

* * *

Much confusion clouded the issue of patent rights, and delayed the availability of the lifesaving serum, perhaps because of the university's handling of it.

Lilly had been licensed to distribute their Insulin exclusively up to 30 May 1923. Until then, the Insulin Committee at Toronto had insisted on restriction of supplies to clinicians only to enable doctors in general practice throughout Canada and the USA to be trained in its use.

It had already been proved that an overdose could kill and their caution was justified, but additional time was needed to receive, assess and answer questions sent from the clinicians themselves.

Eli Lilly's director George Clowes, worried as to what would happen after May when their exclusive mandate ended, bombarded Toronto with correspondence asking for an extension and approval to distribute freely throughout America. If licences were granted to other pharmaceutical manufacturers who were not confronted with the financial expenditure that Lilly had had, then the company would be at a distinct disadvantage.

Their attitude was practical and businesslike, the purpose of their activities being to make money, whereas the university people had no need to be commerce-driven.

Eli Lilly wanted to call their Indianapolis product 'Iletin', which gave rise to suspicion that a patent might be taken out by them in opposition to that taken out in the names of Banting and Best by Toronto University. This was not so, but Lilly had to recoup some of the thousands of dollars spent in their efforts to refine and improve their product. Although the head of the Insulin Committee, Professor Macleod, refused to extend their privilege and the manufacturer graciously accepted this decision, it all added to the delay.

Eventually it became clear that the Toronto Committee would not be ready to grant external licences until much later, and Lilly's fears proved groundless.

It was June 1925 before new American licensees began

distribution, and supplies in the UK in any quantity did not start until April 1923.

The scene became even more complicated by the number of scientists claiming to have made the discovery long before the Toronto team. While the proven reduction of blood sugar by injecting pancreatic extracts by researchers such as Zuelzer (as far back as 1912), Mankowsky, Paulescu and many others, the patents committee recognised the Toronto team because they, and they alone, had refined the extract to a reliable product that enabled people to live almost normal lives.

As the supply of Insulin improved and the wonders it could perform became better known, so did the name of Doctor Frederick Banting. To a lesser degree, the media included Charles Best, and even less still, Professors James Collip and J.J.R. Macleod.

There was a feeling among the lay members of Toronto University board of governors that Banting should be awarded something tangible, especially as some of them looked upon this gentle and self-effacing man (according to their most prominent newspaper) as nothing less than a genius. Among Banting's powerful and influential friends were Elizabeth's Hughes' father Charles (the most politically prominent man in the USA), Professor Henderson, Fitzgerald of Connaught Laboratories, Frederick Allen, Elliot Joslin, Clowes (of Eli Lilly), and hundreds of patients, relatives and doctors, whose praise of him would never be high enough. They generated and fanned the opinion that Banting should receive some spectacular reward for his services to Canada.

The first move was a proposal by a Toronto Conservative MP in the House of Commons in Ottowa that a financial award should be made 'to distinguished scientists like Doctor Frederick Banting and Mr Charles Best. ... Especially when you think of the numbers of our brightest professional men who are leaving Canada for the United States and England. It is time the government of Canada did something to encourage scientific discovery of this kind…'

The proposal was turned down.

Two days later, in the legislature of the province of Toronto in Ontario, the leader of the opposition, Howard Ferguson, proposed that the province should recognise Banting, if the Dominion would not.

The Premier of Ontario, E. C. Drury, promised to look into the matter. It was no coincidence that Fred Banting was an Ontario man…

* * *

The telephone was ringing as Fred unlocked the door to his Bloor Street surgery. No one else had arrived yet. The *Toronto Star* was under his elbow as he made his way into his office. The paper slipped from under his arm to the floor as he unhooked the earpiece from the pedestal.

'That you, Fred?' an excited voice sounded loudly in the listener's ear.

'Yea, yea, it's Fred. What's the noise about?'

'Have you looked at the paper?' Before Fred could retrieve it, the speaker carried on.

'You and Macleod… You've won the Nobel Prize!'

Macleod! A Nobel award! No mention of Best! There seemed no depth to the loathing that Banting felt for the man. As soon as he picked up the copy of the *Star* from the floor, the headline leapt at him. He did not even stop to lock the surgery door as he slammed it, boarded the car and drove to the university. He was intent on battle.

The decision to refuse the prize had already crystallized in his mind. He would sort the little swine out, he had said. 'Just see if I don't!

Fitzgerald was waiting for him at the steps in front of the Medical Building. He could see that Fred was going to rush past him, but he managed catch the arm of the red-faced figure.

'Fred! Stop! Wait a minute. Where are you going?'

'Where am I going? I'm going to tell Macleod just what I think of him. He's engineered this himself. Once more the self-centred figure. I don't want *his* name alongside mine. Never, never, never!'

Fitzgerald took hold of Fred's arm more gently.

'Look, you mustn't go in there in the state you're in. You're not going to do yourself any good and I can tell you that Macleod had nothing to do with this. The Nobel Committee is the authority that decides who gets what, and no outside party is allowed anywhere near them. People can make recommendations, but the Committee alone makes the decision. Calm down, Fred. There's a very important man waiting to see you up in the lab. I think you should see what he has to say before you do anything silly.'

The gentleman was Colonel Albert Gooderham.

As a member of the board of governors and a patron of Connaught Laboratories, he had taken part in an investigation after the ill-advised press report about sole credit for the Insulin research being Macleod's. In an attempt to resolve the bickering, he had asked each member of the team to submit a written version, stage by stage, of the investigations into the pancreatic extracts. When finally submitted, they were never made public. It must have been obvious to the colonel that they were so much at variance that it would be impossible to integrate them in any way.

As Fred Banting and Fitzgerald came into the room, the colonel stood up and extended his hand to Banting.

'Well done, Doctor Banting! My sincerest congratulations. I see Fitzgerald has already met you, but at least I am delighted to be the second to give recognition to your bringing such an honour as the Nobel Prize to your country.'

The words cooled Banting down, but he was still obviously disturbed.

'Thank you, Colonel, but I have made a decision. I will not accept it, indeed I cannot accept it.'

Gooderham was visibly shaken, and sat down on a chair.

'Look here, Banting, you can't behave this way. You have eleven days to get to Stockholm, where the award is to be made. There's a boat sailing from Quebec tomorrow, and you can make it. I want you to be there. You're the first Canadian to win the Nobel. I'll pay all your expenses, only I don't want anything said about it.'

Banting put up his hand, palm outwards in a gesture of rejection, but before he could open his mouth, Gooderham continued.

'I respect your feelings because I know the whole story, but what will the world think when they learn that you've spurned such a prize just because of a difference of opinion? It's the greatest award that can be given a scientist for his work.'

Banting leant back against a bench. He was silent, thinking more calmly.

'All right. I hadn't thought about it from that angle. I'll accept it on condition that my colleague, Charles Best, is also named in the citation.'

That was to prove impossible. Although the Nobel Committee later admitted that the award could have been made to a maximum of three, Best's name was never added.

A telegram came from Banting to Boston, where Charles Best was speaking.

Doctor Joslin was present, and read out the message to the assembly.

'I ascribe to Best equal share in the discovery. Hurt that he is not so acknowledged by Nobel trustees. Will share with him.'

The 'share' that Banting referred to was half of the financial award that went with the prize.

Professor Macleod followed suit by sharing his award with Collip.

On 26 November, Toronto University awarded its Nobel laureates honorary Doctor of Science degrees. Poor Charley Best did not receive one.

CHAPTER 17

The story of Elizabeth Hughes. Banting's favourite patient.

Sons and daughters of wealthy American families had parties, lots of parties, organised by parents who tried to outdo each other in having bigger and better spreads of food: cakes with ever-thicker icing sugar on top and marzipan underneath, sweets, fizzy drinks – everything more lavish than the last.

It was in 1918, when Elizabeth Hughes was eleven, that all her troubles began. There had already been several friends who had had birthday parties that year, but by the time her own arrived, she was losing weight and energy. She had developed a thirst that was unquenchable, and although excited at the prospect of the celebrations, she looked tired and listless even before they started.

Her guests arrived in hordes – smartly turned out little boys, girls in frothy party dresses – to be welcomed at the door, where a maid took their coats and bonnets. Bearing gaudily wrapped gifts, boxes of chocolates, sweets and games, they were ushered to a big dining room, where the table was laden with food.

The cake, complete with lit candles, was ceremoniously brought in, buttermilk flames gleaming in the still air.

It took Elizabeth several attempts to blow them out. The kids stuffed themselves with all they could hold, then games began: blind man's buff, hide and seek, all the usual fun; but Elizabeth's energy ran out and she sat on a settee, watching the others quietly.

Her mother, Antoinette, saw her and went over.

'Are you not feeling too good, dear?' she asked.

The child was pale and looking miserable.

'I'm sorry, Mommy. I'd just like to go to bed. Could I go now?'

Her mother led her upstairs, and the governess took over. It was not the first time she had had to do this. Antoinette contacted parents by telephone, asking if they could collect their children. One by one they disappeared, and the servants began to tidy up.

No one realised that the type of food Elizabeth was eating – the chocolates and sweet cakes – and the lemonade she was drinking, were all worsening her condition.

As their daughter deteriorated from a bright, laughing, energetic child in 1918 to one drowsy and lethargic, patently unwell only a few months later, her parents took her to the finest physicians in Washington, but none was able to discover what was amiss. It was time to seek further afield for help.

When the house was silent after the party, Charles and Antoinette Hughes relaxed in deep armchairs. Charles poured out a nightcap from a decanter, and they began discussing their daughter.

'Charles, we've *got* to do something about Elizabeth. You saw her at the party this evening. She can't tell me what's wrong, other than she can never get enough to drink and she's always terribly tired. It's so unlike her.'

Charles nodded. 'I know. She looks thinner every time I see her. I'm as worried about her as you are, Antoinette.' Taking a sip of brandy, he continued. 'I *have* been thinking about something we could do.'

Elizabeth's father was Charles Edward Hughes, wealthy, one of the most prominent men in American politics and later to run as the Republican candidate for the presidency.

Elizabeth, their youngest daughter, was born in the New York State Governor's house. She wanted for nothing, but did not have the 'show-off 'characteristics of her circle of friends.

Her report cards from school gave her top marks. She was highly intelligent – something that was to help her in the hard times that lay ahead. She was not strongly built, but strikingly pretty.

'I'm doing some legal work for a specialist in diabetes, Doctor Frederick Allen,'Charles began.

Antoinette interrupted sharply.

'Did you say diabetes? What makes you say that?'

Her husband took a sip of brandy.

'I'm not saying she has it for sure, but her symptoms match those of a colleague of mine who developed diabetes and finished up with this specialist. He's setting up what he calls his "physiatric Institute" in Morristown, New York. There's a number of people specialising in diabetes – another is Elliot Joslin. He's in Boston and he's had a practice there for years. Most of his life's been spent on the study of diabetes, and they say he's very good with children. I think we should see if Doctor Allen would examine her – after all I know him personally and my friend got a lot of help there. Maybe Elliot Joslin might see her too – he and Allen are great friends, I believe. If it *is* diabetes, they'll tell us what can be done about it.'

Antoinette said nothing. She was thinking out loud when she murmured 'Diabetes… There's no treatment for it, is there?'

Her husband drained his glass and stood up.

'Well it's something positive, what I'm suggesting, isn't it?'

She nodded. He drew her up and took her in his arms.

'Yes. It's something positive,' he heard her say. 'Nothing much else we can do, is there?'

Charles did not tell her that his colleague had died.

A few days later, Antoinette packed a few items in a small suitcase for her daughter. Doctor Allen had suggested that they bring her to Morristown for a stay at the 'Physiatric Insitute'.

He was waiting for them in front of an imposing mansion house as they climbed out of the chauffeur-driven car. Frederick Allen was tall, heavily built and unsmiling. He stretched out a hand to the

Hughes, then turned to the child. 'And this is Elizabeth?' he asked, patting her head. She smiled politely, and took an instant dislike to him.

A uniformed woman came down the steps to the group. Allen introduced her. 'This is Nurse Tasker. Give the case to her, and she'll take your daughter up to the ward. Say goodbye to your mother and father.'

Elizabeth had never been separated from them apart from a few nights with relatives or young friends. She disliked being far from home, her parents so far away, but forced herself to see things through.

She hugged Charles and kissed him, but was reluctant to part from her mother. Nurse Tasker picked up the case and touched the child's elbow.

'Come along now. You'll see your parents soon again.'

They set off ahead of her parents Antoinette turned away, managing to hold back tears as they followed them into the building.

Doctor Allen took Charles and his wife to his office. Once they were seated in front of him, he opened a notepad and unscrewed a fountain pen.

'Now then, your daughter is obviously not well. I need to know all about her, her behaviour, her development of illness, anything at all.'

The Hugheses described the years of happiness and wellbeing, her sudden decline, loss of weight, insatiable thirst. After taking copious notes, Frederick Allen replaced the cap on the pen and closed the notebook.

'From what you've said, it's almost certain that your daughter has diabetes. We treat our patients by removing *all* carbohydrate from their food in the first place. After a few days, we gradually introduce a little at a time until we find the level they can tolerate. No sweets, jams, bread or biscuits are allowed. Rusks are all we allow, with lean meat, fruit and eggs. All vegetables are boiled. You must not bring any food here when visiting. It's a harsh regime, particularly for children. Is your daughter able to take instructions like that without failing? The entire success depends on staying on the diet.'

Charles spoke firmly. 'I can assure you that Elizabeth is quite capable of absolute obedience. She'll do what she's told.'

James and his wife exchanged looks.

'We're pleased that you've been able to diagnose the cause of her illness,' Antoinette said, 'but isn't it correct to say that people who have diabetes just die?'

Doctor Allen replied sharply.

'Now you mustn't say that. Diabetes is not necessarily fatal. Some people live for years, many years if the diet is controlled. I can only say that the diagnosis is fairly certain. I'll be able to confirm it in a day or two once tests have been completed. Many researchers are investigating treatment that might cure, or at least allow diabetics to recover lost health, but the secret has, so far, evaded them. Now, I suggest that you do not see your daughter again for the present. Just leave us to get on with our investigations. I'll send a letter to you in due course. She's in safe hands, I can assure you.' It was clear, as he stood up, that the interview was at an end. A servant girl took the pair back down to the car park.

Her parents went back to the car and started off back to Washington. There was not much conversation between them on the long drive. There was little they could have said in any case. A visit to Joslin's clinic at Boston had resulted in the same diagnosis.

Elizabeth climbed the stairs laboriously with the nurse. The first floor ward was bright and cheerfully decorated. The four women in the room were not cheerful. They were gaunt and white. One was reading a book, the others gazing at nothing. Two looked up as Nurse Tasker and her charge came in, without changing their expressions.

G. Barclay Robertson

'This'll be your bed, Elizabeth. These ladies will be with you here. They know how to fetch me if you need anything. I'll be back later to tell you about the rules. You haven't brought any food in with you, have you?'

Elizabeth shook her head.

'You can start by unpacking and putting your belongings in that locker.'

She put the suitcase on the bed. Elizabeth unlatched the lid and began lifting items out as the nurse left. A few minutes later, she saw the ward door begin to open. A small boy put his head round it. She smiled but he did not respond, other than coming slowly in and standing on the other side of the bed. He looked about nine. Without any introduction, he spoke.

'Have you got anything to eat?'

Elizabeth was beginning to learn just how important food was to her fellow residents.

'Are you so hungry you've got to ask *me*? I've just arrived.'

The boy nodded. 'I watched you come. You don't know what they do to you here, do you?'

She shook her head.

'Well, they starve you. There's one day a week, fasting days they call them, you don't get any food at all, and precious little the rest. Will you have visitors coming in?' Without waiting for an answer, he asked if they might be bringing any food with them.

'Look, you'll need to wait until I see what Nurse Tasker has to say.'

'*Her*! She's the one that finds out if you've eaten anything extra. I get so hungry, I even took some of the birdseed from its holder in the cage downstairs, and she gave me a row for that.'

'I think you should go back to wherever you came from. I don't want to hear any more about things like that,' she said, turning towards the window. When she looked round, he was gone.

One of the adults got up from her chair.

'Did I hear your name is Elizabeth? I'm Margaret. Let me show you where to put your things. There's a space for them down here.'

The youngster was pleased to find a friend.

It was beginning to get dark. She took the toilet bag her mother had packed for her and went through to a bathroom off the ward. As usual, she was thirsty. Water from the cold tap only helped a little, and she was also hungry.

She undressed, washed herself thoroughly, and returned wearing her nightdress. The beds had all been turned back and as she clambered in, Doctor Allen appeared with Nurse Tasker. There was a mumbled conversation at the door. The doctor disappeared and the nurse came over to Elizabeth. She listened patiently as the 'rules' were spelled out to her.

'You can get up during the day and take walks through the gardens, but you mustn't go alone. Ask one of the ladies to go with you.' Nurse Tasker had something with her, hidden beneath a white cloth. 'Now this here's to use when you go to pass water. Every time you go, take this with you 'cos we need it to test for sugar.'

As she spoke, she drew the cloth away. 'It' turned out to be a white china bedpan. Elizabeth had noticed the others always carried them when they visited the lavatory. Now she knew what they were for...

'How do you mean: "test for sugar"?' she asked.

Nurse Tasker continued. 'It lets us see how well you're doing here, tells us if your food is too high or too low in carbohydrate.'

All this was new to the ward's latest patient, but she was tired.

The nurse was tucking her in when she remembered that her furry teddy bear was not beside her, and fished it from the locker. Nurse Tasker slipped it under the sheets.

She buried her face in its soft body. It smelled of home.

She woke to the clattering noise of the venetian blinds being drawn up. She dutifully took the bedpan with her to the bathroom, washed, and returned to bed. A girl appeared with trays, one of which she brought to Elizabeth.

'Breakfast time,' she called. Breakfast was a boiled egg, a small piece of toast and a cup of weak tea. At home, the maid would be serving cereal with fruit, crisp bacon and egg, toast from a well-laden rack, butter and maple syrup.

A different nurse collected all the bedpans. At midday, Nurse Tasker came back.

'Elizabeth, I'm afraid your sugar levels are way too high. I know you'll find it hard, but your diet will have to be cut down a great deal from what you got through at home.'

The girl in the bed glowered at her. 'Is this the only way you can make me well?' she demanded. 'I never thought it'd be like this.'

'Look, trust us. You won't be nearly so thirsty in a few days…'

The nurse was right. Because of her spartan diet, Elizabeth's sugar levels fell. So did her thirst and so did her weight.

Elizabeth sent letters to her parents every few days. She studied her lessons hard from the schoolbooks her teachers had given her, and it was a means of passing the time as weeks wore on. Soon after she arrived at Morristown, she wrote, 'Mister Allen is such a grim man. Never says anything friendly, in fact seldom says anything at all. Always keeps insisting on people doing what they're told. How I long for an ice cream, chocolate, custard, home-baked rolls, even a bit of toast. We're not allowed any of those.'

Another letter spoke of events that took place during her sojourn in Morristown.

'Tommy, the boy who asked me if I could give him anything to eat the day I arrived, you remember? I came across him sucking toothpaste out of the tube in the bathroom another day. I haven't seen him for a while now…'

None of the nurses told her she was suffering from diabetes. No one told her Tommy was dead.

When admitted, Elizabeth weighed seventy-five pounds. After

the few weeks sticking closely to Allen's disciplines, she was sent home weighing fifty-five. She was also given a diet sheet, with instructions to adhere closely to it.

From the age of eleven until she was fifteen and taken from Morristown to Toronto General Hospital on 12 August 1922, Elizabeth was virtually an invalid. She had a Joslin-trained nurse who lived in, looked after her, and supervised her diet.

On her fourteenth birthday, her party had just as much food on the tables as usual for her guests, but her cake was made from a hat-box covered with pink and white paper, with candles stuck in it. On family picnics, she had her own small frying pan and spirit stove, with which the nurse made omelettes for her. The other youngsters had chops, corn on the cob, watermelon, sandwiches, biscuits and cakes.

She stuck valiantly to Allen's 'starvation' diet, but tonsillitis and colds pulled her down in 1920. The next two years saw most of the remaining flesh disappear from her body. By 1922 she was finding difficulty in standing without help. In the spring, the Hughes decided to send her for a holiday in the sun in an effort to build her up.

They sent for Elliot Joslin. A few days later, he called at the Hughes' home in Washington.

The doctor was shown into the drawing room. Charles and Antoinette led Elizabeth forward as the maid poured out coffee and offered biscuits.

'Elizabeth. How do you do again,' the doctor said, extending his hand to her. He could feel the bones through papery skin, but she shook his hand firmly enough.

Solemn eyes gazed at him. 'Hi there. Doctor Allen has told me about you. Do you mind if I sit down?'

She was an extremely polite young lady, but Joslin saw at once how little strength she had; it was obvious in the way she had to lever herself up onto the seat. Picking up the coffee cup, he spoke directly to her.

'Now, I've been asked to come and talk with you about this marvellous holiday to Bermuda your folks have been suggesting. What do you think about that?'

The girl looked at him reservedly.

'Well… I'm told the sun'll do me a lot of good. If it makes me feel a bit better than I am right now, I'll lie out in it all day!'

Joslin nodded. 'You *will* feel the better of it, but you mustn't get too much. It'll do more harm than good if you get sunstroke. Stick to an hour in the morning and the same after lunch. Now I must tell you Doctor Allen is very proud of you because of the way you've stuck to his diet. That'll be very important too while you're away.'

'He never tells *me* he's pleased,' Elizabeth told him. 'In fact he *never* tells anybody he's pleased, but yes, I do try to do what I'm told.'

A hint of a smile crept over the corner of Joslin's lips.

'Yes, I know he's not a fellow to cheer people up a lot, but he's a good man, and means only the best for you.'

Elizabeth took to this man who smiled so readily and spoke so highly of the unpopular doctor she disliked so much. As he left, having issued instructions to the nurse for the voyage, he said farewell to his patient.

'Enjoy the holiday, Elizabeth, and do what Nurse Blanche says. I'll pray for you. God bless and care for you.' He was a man of deep faith.

Nurse Blanche and Elizabeth set sail for Bermuda in the spring. Elizabeth insisted on mounting the gangplank without help, but was confined to her bed in the stateroom for the next two days. The nurse noticed that the little strength her patient had had disappeared because of the effort to reach the ship's deck alone. Eventually, they spent much of their time sitting out on deckchairs in the sun.

Elizabeth enjoyed a few extras in the dining room, putting on one or two precious pounds. The Bermudan hotel catered for her diet meticulously, but a few days after their arrival, an epidemic of stomach trouble, diarrhoea and sickness swept the island.

Elizabeth had no resistance and, to the nurse's horror, she contracted the illness. Within a day it was plain that they would have to return to Washington.

* * *

Screens round a bed in the diabetic ward at Toronto General Hospital meant one of two things: the patient was severely ill or dying. The former was the case for Elizabeth Hughes, who lay behind the screens that August of 1922. The chart at the foot of the bed logged her name; her age, fifteen; her weight on admission, forty-five pounds. She was five feet tall. Fast, shallow breathing made the sheets over her rise and fall rapidly. Her eyes were closed.

Her presence there had come about by constant pressure from two sources. There had been a number of letters from her mother, Antoinette, pleading for her daughter's admission to the only hospital in the world where diabetes was being treated successfully. Her letters became increasingly desperate as Elizabeth's illness got worse, but Doctor Banting's replies were always the same: 'We are unable to help at present...'

They came from the biggest heap of duplicated replies on his desk: the 'no hope' pile.

More petitions followed, another from Elizabeth's mother describing her as 'our pitifully depleted and reduced daughter,' offers of money, 'as much as may be asked,' and others, but the pleadings had to be rejected.

'It is not a matter of money; it is a matter of insufficient medication to treat the number of patients. Only the most severely ill are being admitted.' Such desperate pleadings made Fred Banting's distress increase more than ever. Three long years under the control of Frederick Allen, together with the disastrous Bermuda holiday, had brought Elizabeth Hughes almost to death's door.

Frailer day by day, 'surviving' on the dreaded carbohydrate-restricted diet, Allen himself took the last step that finally brought her to the hospital. He personally asked Banting to treat her, realising that she could not last much longer. For Banting, it was the second time of meeting. Allen had almost made an exhibit of her to him as a prime example of how his treatment extended the lives of those who could stand it.

The severity of his discipline made many unable to do so for long.

They were not of Elizabeth Hughes' calibre.

The screens moved aside and a white-coated doctor stepped over to the bed. Taking a stethoscope, he warmed the pad in a palm and drew the bedclothes down. The girl opened her eyes just then.

'Well, hi there, Elizabeth. D'you remember me – Doctor Banting? We met at the clinic in Morristown when I went there a while ago.'

Elizabeth gazed at him calmly. She found his country accent unexpected, but it was warm and friendly. And he smiled with his eyes too. Little had happened to make her smile over the past few years. He wore thin, brass-framed glasses, she noticed.

'Yes, I remember. Are you going to make me better? Will I have to keep on with this awful diet?'

'Sure I'm gonna make you well again. You'll be running around like new in just a little while, and you'll be able to eat much, much more, very soon, probably today. How's that?'

Elizabeth fell silent, unable to say anything at the very thought of tucking into something more than vegetables boiled three times to remove all the carbohydrate, lean meat, eggs, and tasteless rusks.

Banting helped her to sit up, and used his stethoscope, then tapped and probed her pathetically wasted body. Even he was surprised that she was still alive. Her skin was stretched tightly over ribs like a starved animal, the stomach grotesquely swollen, her arms stick-like. He took in the bare patches on her skull where hair had fallen out, the sunken eye sockets and as he bent over her to complete the examination, the smell like rotting apples on her breath. Her blood was showing enormously high levels of sugar. Ketones were present in the urine.

She was seriously ill. Insulin treatment would have to start at once if she was to stay alive much longer. Determination was the only thing keeping her heart beating, but the stage was set for a tragic finale.

A nurse trundled a set of cast-iron platform scales over to the bedside.

'Can you manage to stand on these for me?' Banting asked.

She levered her legs out and stood shakily on the metal plate.

'Ow! That's cold!' she announced.

The doctor apologised. 'I should've known better and put a towel down for you, but I'll be done in a second.'

The balance tilted at forty-five pounds. He helped her back into bed.

'Now I'll be back shortly. You'll get an injection of stuff called Insulin and it'll be a bit sore, but in a few hours, you'll begin to feel a lot better *and* you'll get a good, square meal.'

'If I get something decent to eat, Doctor Banting, it'll be worth any pain,' she answered.

The dieticians tending the patients in the diabetic ward studied the diet sheet given to them by Fred Banting. They could not take in what it said.

'Increase to 1,220 calories – that's preposterous!' one said huffily.

'It'll kill her!' declared another. 'All my life, diabetics only lived a little while anyway – always on a strict food regime.'

Even Doctor Campbell found the sheet unacceptable. He met Banting in the ward later.

'Look here, Doctor, the girl's only been put on Insulin three days ago. I know her blood sugar's much lower, but you can't break every rule in diabetes control like this.'

Banting stared him out.

'You've seen her. No wonder she's so emaciated. At Allen's clinic, she's been fading away at fewer than 900 calories a day. No wonder they call it the starvation diet at Morristown. Let me be, will you. It'll work all right.'

By the end of the following week, Elizabeth was tucking into meat pies, bread sandwiches, spaghetti, jellies and milk puddings – a total of 2,240 calories: the normal level for a girl of fifteen. Within thirty days, her weight was going up by two and half pounds a week.

Long letters to her mother showed the delight she felt at her emergence from the years of misery. 'To think I'll lead a normal, healthy existence is beyond all comprehension,' she wrote. 'Oh, it is simply too wonderful for words, this stuff,' she said a month later, writing about Insulin. 'Doctor Banting is such a marvellous man.'

Reporters began to descend on her, and the media picked up the story. It was published throughout North America:

MIRACULOUS RECOVERY FOR DYING GIRL. BANTING DOES IT AGAIN

Fred met up with another old friend from his early days at the university: another doctor. His name was D.E. Robertson. It was the day the *Toronto Star* printed the front page article about Elizabeth Hughes and Banting. They had lunch together in the university's faculty club.

'You're going to be famous, Fred,' he said. 'Look, is that the only suit you've got?

Fred looked shamefaced. 'Well… Yes it is.'

When lunch finished, they went to the best tailor in Toronto. A fitter came forward, a tape measure round his neck.

'Make this man a suit,' Robertson told him. 'And an overcoat too.'

A wire arrived from Clowes at Eli Lilly on 19 August: 'INSULIN PRODUCTION IN BULK THIS WEEK. WORKING PERFECTLY'

Banting and Best met that night in their old haunt, the speakeasy in town.

Fred lifted his tankard and clinked it against Charley's.

'We're there, Charley, we're there. No more abscesses, no more failures with unstable Insulin.'

Charley stretched his hand over the table and squeezed Fred's so hard he winced.

'And plenty of it, too…'

Jim Havens in Rochester was given the new product and, snatched from death's door, began to pick up within days.

Elizabeth Hughes, filling out, developing into the beautiful teenager she should have been, wrote again, almost unable to find words that described her feelings over the change.

'Isn't this unspeakably wonderful?'

Elliot Joslin paid a visit to Toronto Hospital one day in September. He too was receiving quantities of Lilly's Insulin, and the same remarkable recoveries were happening to the little patients at his clinic in Boston. The relief brought to the hungry residents at Allen's Morristown 'Physiatric Hospital' was equally dramatic.

There was to be a gathering of doctors and researchers at Toronto Hospital in the afternoon to allow them to see and examine the patients in the diabetic ward. Banting and Joslin met just outside the ward, where Walter Campbell, Professor Graham, Frederick Allen and Rawle Geyelin joined them. Geyelin was a keen photographer as well as a researcher, and had been making records of the 'before and after' transformations in various patients. Doctor Campbell pushed the doors open, remarking to Joslin, over his shoulder, 'You'll hardly recognise one patient here when you see her…'

Elizabeth Hughes was used to visitors. Press photographers and reporters, scientists, diabetologists and researchers descended on her every day. She complained in ever more prolific letters to her parents about the pestering, the intrusive, personal questions, and the flashes from press cameras that startled her so often.

When the sound of voices came from behind the ward doors, she put down the magazine she was reading, smoothed down her dress and prepared for the next onslaught. But it was not newsmen this time. The first person she saw was Elliot Joslin.

She threw the paper on the floor and ran to him. As he grasped her in his arms, Fred Banting came close behind. He also was given a clinging hug.

She grinned at them all.

'Gosh! I haven't seen you since the Bermuda holiday, Doctor Joslin. Look a bit different now, don't I?' She gave a little pirouette, holding her dress out like a ballet dancer.

Frederick Allen was given a welcome too, but only a shy handshake. The sight of him reminded her too much of the grim experiences at Morristown. Campbell took her arm and led her back to the charts at her bed.

'Just look at Elizabeth's records here, gentlemen. The increase in weight is quite staggering. The blood sugar graphs are steady, and near normal.'

They passed the clipboards to each other and studied them, one by one.

Elliot Joslin could hardly take in what he was seeing. Here was a patient who, when they met after the disastrous Bermuda trip, was like a skeleton, not expected to live more than a few days, unable to stand.

Today he was looking at a slim teenager, bright-eyed, smiling and plainly happy, who had actually *run* towards the doctors, clutching them, welcoming them with enthusiasm and cheerfulness.

Standing back a little, he could hardly take his eyes from her. He was obviously thinking quietly before he began to speak, quoting from Ezekiel's Old Testament story of the valley of dry bones. As he began, the others fell silent.

'And behold, there were very many in the open valley; and lo, they were very dry.

And He said to me, "Son of Man, can these bones live?"

And lo, the sinews and flesh came upon them and the skin covered them.

Then said He unto me, "Prophesy unto the wind. Prophesy, Son of Man and say unto the wind 'Thus saith the Lord God: come from the four winds, O breath, and breathe upon these slain, that they may live. So I prophesied as He commanded me, and they lived and stood up upon their feet, an exceeding great army..."

It was plain to the good doctor that Ezekiel's miracle was taking place right there in front of him.

CHAPTER 18

1923–1934

Beds in the diabetic ward at Toronto General Hospital were at a premium. Elizabeth Hughes was making a spectacular recovery, but Banting wanted to keep an eye on her for a while. She was his star case, an ideal example of success that could only be attributed to himself. To allow one more bed to be cleared, her parents agreed to rent rooms in the nearby Anselma Apartments, where their daughter and Nurse Blanche could stay. His calls were frequent, something to which Elizabeth looked forward, as there was little to do, other than walk in the park and the occasional visit from her father and mother. She was beautiful, with the bloom of youth and good health transforming her from the wretched state of a few months before.

Banting called one spring day, carried out his blood tests, and sat down for a short chat.

'How would you and Blanche like to come round to my laboratory and see where your Insulin was discovered? If it were not for that, you'd not be talking to me now, Elizabeth.'

She gazed at him, wide eyed. 'Gee! That'd be great. Yes I'd love to come. When?'

'Tomorrow evening, if you're free?'

The nurse was unable to come, but agreeable that her charge should accept the invitation.

He took her to Connaught Laboratories first. She wrote her mother about the tour later:

'That enormous plant runs night and day, with men working in relays. … Later, we went to his laboratory, where Doctor Banting and his colleague Mister Best told me how they made the great discovery. There were some paintings on the walls – his own work. He is the *most* talented man… Gracious! I felt so grown up, going out with a *man* alone, at night! They were both *so* charming...'

While she wrote so enthusiastically about her newfound life-style, there were times when the she was in pain when the Insulin was poor in quality and the amounts had to be doubled, even tre-bled. Yet she never complained. Never.

The first six months of 1923 brought fame and fortune to Frederick Banting on a scale he could never have imagined in his wildest dreams.

Queen's University in Kingston, Ontario awarded him his first honorary degree; the Ontario Government decided to establish the Banting and Best Chair of Medical Research at Toronto University, funded by a grant of $10,000. Banting was to head it as professor, with an annual salary of $5000. One of Banting's hero worshippers was George 'Billy' Ross, a well-known and respected man in both medical and political spheres. His father had been a Liberal premier of Ontario, and he was friendly with Sir William Mulock, an old fel-low statesman of the Prime Minister, Mackenzie King. Many other friends had strong connections with MPs and government officials. When Ross continued to urge the Canadian government in Ottowa to grant an annuity in recognition of 'Banting's Discovery', this was passed in the sum of $7,500.

Ross also approached the Toronto Academy of Medicine, sug-gesting that a statement be issued that Banting and Best were to have priority in the matter of the Insulin discovery. This was carried out immediately.

At the time in 1923 that news about all this reached Banting, he was on board the *Empress of France* en route to England. The trip was to be one of combined business and pleasure, of conferences, sightseeing and rest. He sent a wire to Best expressing regret that he was not to receive an equal share of the awards. 'Surely blessings are falling on us fast enough now though. We must keep our heads.'

Invitations kept arriving to speak at seminars and research con-ferences, all with large fees, always with the offer of accommodation at top-class hotels. It was as well that Professor Henderson was with him to help with replies.

Then came a reply from Charles Best. The tone was sharp. He was clearly disappointed and angry about lack of recognition and the financial benefits that Banting was receiving, mainly due, he felt, to Ross's promotion of Fred – and only Fred.

Letters and wires flew between the pair. Banting did his utmost to restore the rapport that had almost always existed between the two, but their friendship remained strained.

In Toronto, Professor Fitzgerald and other powerful members on the university board made approaches to Prime Minister Mackenzie King to include Best alongside Banting, but it was too late. No action was taken.

Banting was concerned about what was happening, or rather what was *not* happening to Best. He discussed with Henderson the suitability of making his anger public.

'Leave it alone, Fred. You'll be able to sort it out once you get back to Canada.'

The *Toronto Star*'s reporter was one Ernest Hemmingway, a name later to become almost as famous as Frederick Banting's. If he had done his job properly and got the truth out, Charley Best's fame might have come more rapidly, but Best had no friends on a par with Banting's…

The whirl of press conferences in London, speeches, lectures and interviews, was overwhelming. Meetings with medical experts – the highest in the land – had been arranged. Banting's diaries record his audience with the King, George V.

'His Majesty was most gracious, and in a moment I was completely at ease and we were talking about hospitals and research work. I was amazed at the knowledge the man had.'

Velyien Henderson was there, constantly at his elbow, advising him on matters such as how to behave in the presence of royalty, how long each speech should last, prompting him on what to say. The main problem was Banting's accent; no amount of tutoring improved it.

One of the first events after arriving in London was an appearance at an international congress of surgeons. The speaker preceding Banting was Doctor Serge Voronoff, the surgeon who introduced the transplantation of monkey testicles for elderly gentlemen, thus, he claimed, restoring their sex drive.

It was nonsense, but wealthy old men underwent the surgery in droves. They paid a hefty fee, suffered pain for months, and yet declared firmly that they had recovered long-lost youth.

Doctor Voronoff spoke in immaculate French, and was enthusiastically applauded.

Banting's lecture was delivered in his Canadian country accent, in mumbles barely audible at times.

The elite audience stole looks at each other, became restless and shuffled their feet. Banting stopped speaking, gathered his notes, and left the room. It was a minute or so before the audience realised that he had reached the end of his discourse and began feeble applause.

The reporter covering the conference described Banting as 'A doer, not a speaker'.

Lectures in Edinburgh with Professor Macleod followed, where Banting fared better, talking about Insulin to clinicians – people who were actually working with the wonder drug and on a par with himself. He remained cold towards Macleod, and conversed only when necessary until the professor left. Banting once more started on his constant tirade against Macleod.

It began to bring increasing concern to Velyien Henderson.

'Fred, listen to me a minute,' he said over the dinner table. They were relaxing after a busy day in London, when two speeches had been made in the afternoon following a tour of a large hospital in the morning. 'You'll have to watch what you're saying about JJR. Every talk you give, you bring up the subject of professors who have no original ideas, don't attend research sessions, and don't help with money. It's too much, Fred. You must remember that JJR has many friends here. You did give him a promise that you'd stop all that a while back. Rest assured, word *will* get back to him, and that'll not do you any good at all.'

His friend was doing his utmost to make Fred see reason. The *Toronto Star* newsman with them was attending every function, taking copious notes.

'You keep telling people that his name always comes first in papers and lectures he presents. I don't want to contradict you, but he did agree after a row with you before, that the names of the four researchers were to come in alphabetical order, which put yours first. That has happened in most of the press reports I've seen. In fact the rest of the team is often not mentioned at all. The documents used with JJR's name heading them is because it's standard practice in university papers for the head of department to do this; the research *is* in his name, after all.'

Fred lit a cigarette and twirled the stem of his wine glass

'I don't need to worry about him now. I'll say what I like. It's all true anyway; I'm not lying, and I can hardly be blamed for telling the truth.'

Saddened, Henderson realised he was not going to get anywhere. He had done his best, and it was pointless to try to stop Fred from pursuing his headlong criticism of the man who had set him off on the first steps to fame.

Paris concluded the tour. It had changed vastly in the five years since the end of the war. Fashionable clothing was on display in the shop windows, the streets were well lit, and good food was being served at tables lining the boulevards.

It was during a meeting at the prestigious Societe de Biologie that a remarkable event took place. One of France's most respected endocrinologists, Eugene Gley, stood up and asked that a sealed envelope that he had lodged with the Societe in 1905, be opened.

The papers inside revealed that he had been experimenting with pancreatic extracts as far back as 1900. His processes were almost identical to Banting's, and injections of his extracts also substantially reduced blood sugar levels in diabetic dogs. The documents were genuine and stated that Gley had not had the financial resources to proceed further. His last paper set out the need to refine the product to enable production of a reliable and stable serum.

It was a peculiar thing to do. His gesture did nothing for anyone. Had he published the results of his researches, others with better cash backing would have taken his work forward. Insulin might well have been saving lives a quarter of a century sooner, but he simply went on to congratulate Macleod on having brought about *Une grande simplification* of his process.

What his odd conduct did however, was to prove that Professor Macleod's warning to Banting in 1921 was correct. Long, long before, others had adopted the same techniques as the 'idea' that the surgeon had outlined at the beginning of his research. It also increased Banting's fury about Macleod.

'He put Gley up to this,' he spat out angrily to the *Star* reporter. 'It was *my* idea, and mine alone, that brought success to the arrival of Insulin.'

The words appeared verbatim in the most widely read newspaper in Toronto, and in the American press as well.

Banting gave over to his cousin, Fred Hipwell, the Bloor Street practice, and could have spent the rest of his life doing quiet research in the Banting and Best Institute at the university or practising medicine, but he felt that there were other unsolved mysteries to be explored.

He tried to find out if the use of X-rays might destroy the Islets of Langerhans. His 'idea' there was to prevent the onset of hypogly-caemia – the dangerously low blood sugars – which had killed so many of Collip's rabbits. It seemed pointless, as the answer was to determine the amount of Insulin to inject after blood testing. Several other avenues of research into cancers, bacterial toxins and the production of adrenaline only succeeded in the deaths of more dogs – fifty-six in all.

That figure did not include a huge number of rabbits and guinea pigs sacrificed in various other investigations. As far as the adrena-line investigation went, other far more experienced researchers were already greatly more advanced in the subject, yet Banting seemed to know nothing about them. Seeking another success such as Insulin failed dramatically, partially due to another press release claiming that Professor Banting had again produced a remarkable product, but that it could not be described at this stage. Sufferers from all kinds of illness such as cancers, ulcers and arthritis descended on the university, all hoping that the latest discovery might help them. Some who queued and waited to see the genius could not walk. Their friends brought them in wheelchairs.

Banting had to make an embarrassing climbdown, and no more was heard of his latest production. A comment he made in a letter to Rawle Geyelin showed how miserable he felt when no results matched the brilliance with which he was being credited. 'I stand in a very precarious position, with so many people expecting some-thing, and I have nothing to offer.'

Sadie Gairns had a medical training which led to her elevation to laboratory assistant to Banting over at the Research Department. She was also his secretary, where her organising ability made sure that Banting's appointments were kept on time.

She got a shock one day when Fred walked into her office and declared, 'I'm getting married this afternoon.'

'For goodness sake...' was all she could think of to say. 'What next?'

There was a hint of sadness mixed with surprise in her face as she heard his words.

Frederick Banting was one of the most eligible men in Toronto. Famous, still youthful at thirty-two, quite good looking although becoming slightly stooped. The twinkle in his eye had always attracted girls. That year of 1923 his income was $13000, the future was secure, and funds were freely available for any amount of research he wanted to do.

While young girls even took to training as nurses at the General Hospital, hoping to persuade him to date them, he was caught out several times. Double dating one, a young nurse on day shift, the other on nights, the former had a sudden change of shift and ran round to his apartment to tell him. She was confronted with the other nurse just leaving.

Even Fred couldn't explain his way out of that situation!

Another young woman, Marion Robertson, an X-ray technician at the hospital, attracted Fred's attention more strongly than any of the others. Slim and vivacious, she was blue eyed, fair haired and highly intelligent. Daughter of a doctor, she conversed knowledgeably about medical matters and to both, invitations to society gatherings became increasingly frequent.

For Fred, the pathway to love was not to be smooth. Edith Roach had parted company after many years. Trying to see her again several times, the attempts resulted in sadness.

Her family felt that Banting should not be allowed to walk out and leave her uncompensated, then stage a comeback as if nothing had happened, so an agreement was drawn up.

Banting was to pay $2000 and hand over the diamond engagement ring. He was to sever all connections with Edith after that.

A day later, Edith sent a personal letter to him. It was ardent, but not over-emotional. The words told of her sincere love of him… 'the love of our youth. I have faith in you, trust, respect and admiration, for your good points are many, and these will stay with me'.

Edith married some years later, never had any children, and never met Fred again. He was later to wish he *had* married her.

The fascination with Marion rushed ahead at breakneck speed. The sudden decision to get married may have been for a reason. Marion had an unsigned letter delivered on 3 June, almost certainly from a girl with whom Fred had formed an attachment a short while earlier. It warned Marion not to become involved with him. 'I am not the only girl he has fooled,' she wrote. 'So others may be heard from. I know you are a nice girl…'

At 3.00 p.m. on 4 June 1924, Marion and Fred were married in the home of her uncle, Doctor James Caven.

Some of the girls who had known the groom from the Philathea Bible Class days heard about it, and waited for them to come out of the house. They billed and cooed at the handsome, smiling pair as they tripped down the steps.

One dewy-eyed spectator was heard to say, 'It's the beginning of a beautiful romance…'

It certainly started well. A couple of weeks before the wedding, Fred telephoned Marion in the X-ray Department,

'Come over right now. We're going to have a great honeymoon, Marion. In Jamaica. All expenses paid. Come over to my office, and I'll tell you all about it.'

The international 'Conference on Health Problems in Tropic America' was to be held by the United Fruit Company in Kingston, Jamaica. Specialists in tropical diseases were to present speeches to the gathering, all expenses paid. Banting was invited to give a speech on the Insulin discovery.

The doctors brought their wives and girlfriends, the company paid the bills, and between each short lecture the medical men attended dinners, dances, tours of the firm's banana republics, and resided at the best hotel in Kingston.

A few minutes before he was due to start his lecture, Fred remarked to Marion, 'Y'know, this is a conference on tropical diseases. I can't think what I'm doing here. Anyway, enjoy it. It's free!'

He had been scribbling something on a scrap of paper; he leant over and handed it to his new wife. It ran:-

'Why I am here
Is not quite clear
Since diabetes
Of all diseases
is not contagious
in any stages.'

The wedding night was not a success. Perhaps Fred had drunk too much, but he told a close friend about it later.

'I knew from that night that my marriage was a mistake.'

On their return home and from that point on, Marion was to find Fred a pretty rough diamond. Attempts to mould him to the image she had envisaged when they first began their intense relationship did not succeed. Rows were frequent, often over his appearance.

Arguments were constantly happening.

'Look, Fred, can you not change for dinner when you come back from the lab? There's a distinct smell of dogs coming from you, and we have guests arriving any minute.'

He glared at her and lit a cigarette. Marion did not smoke.

'If your guests don't like the smell of me, they'll leave quicker, and that'll suit me fine.'

He would thrust slippers onto his feet and, sitting down at the fire, demand the newspaper. Grubby shoes were dumped on the hearth until Marion removed them.

The usual behaviour at the table was for Fred to maintain a surly silence. The smart guests thought, to begin with, that the great scientist was exhausted after a long day at the lab, probably working on some brilliant new idea along the same lines as Insulin.

'And what new investigation are you working on now, Professor?'

They would be met with a curt reply. 'I'm not able to tell you anything about it just now…'

Marion became increasingly frustrated. Her friends were beginning to find excuses for not responding to her invitations.

She was a dedicated socialite. Enjoying company, sparkling conversation, dining out, going to theatres and operas; she lived on a totally different plane to Fred. Her husband was a grown-up farm boy, with manners and accent to match. His feet seemed incapable of following dance steps simply because he had never learned any. At society functions, other men had to ask her to dance, which she usually accepted. This would bring an angry comment from Fred.

'Listen Marion. That young fellow LeBourdaise's got his eye on you. He was dancing with you more than half the evening.'

'And what were *you* doing with Blodwen Davies then?'

There was no answer to that one. He *had* spent most of the time with the girl, even more than Marion and LeBourdaise had spent together.

Their first home was built to order – a handsome, three-storey house on Avenue Street, near the Bloor Street practice.

Fred had rooms upstairs, where he had a study and more bedrooms. They settled down to the usual pattern of the breadwinner being the husband, the wife the home keeper.

Whether boredom or just plain incompatibility started their sleeping in separate rooms or not, the couple eventually agreed that the only way they could live together was to allow the other to lead life in their own way. Marion could entertain male friends; Fred could have girlfriends. In this way, they could stay under the same roof as if still happily married, but between the lack of success with his researches at the Institute and the awareness that his marriage was breaking down, Fred became seriously depressed. Alcohol always seemed to help, so a bottle of rye was always hidden in the study. It had to be replaced every other day.

Meanwhile something was happening at the university, something about which Frederick Banting had no inkling, but in which he had had a hand, perhaps unconsciously. A discussion was taking place up in the professor's office between Macleod and his secretary. As usual, immaculately dressed, the breast-pocket handkerchief carefully arranged with two points showing, his dark moustache drawing a scrupulously trimmed line across his face, there was never a hair out of place, but there was a change in him that day.

Stella took the opened mail through to him one morning in 1927. The sun was shining through the big windows, casting a diagonal shadow across his face. She had noticed for some time that lines were showing there, and he was not as bright and cheerful as usual.

'Here's the mail, Professor; not so much today. Would you like your coffee now?'

'Yes please, Stella. Bring one through for yourself too. There's something I'd like to talk with you about, and there will be some dictation as well.'

When she returned with the tray, she filled the two cups and sat down in the upright chair she used for dictation sessions. Taking sips from the cup, she waited for Macleod to begin, however it was not dictatation that began his conversation.

.

'Stella, you've been my secretary for a long, long time. You've been the most efficient and tactful one I've ever had, and you've calmed the waters at many a troubled meeting here.'

She listened intently, beginning to wonder if he was leading up to terminating her job, but this was not so.

'You've also been a frequent guest at our home, where my wife and I have grown to feel that you are a friend, a very deep friend, one whose understanding is valued and treasured. You are aware, as so many are, that Doctor Banting has been making harsh and unjustified comments about me and the treatment he has received at the university?'

Stella nodded slightly and said, gently, 'Yes, Professor, I'm afraid I've heard all about it.'

He picked up one of the letters from the pile of mail and held it up.

'I've been waiting for this. It's the confirmation of an offer from Aberdeen University. They want me to become Regius Professor of Physiology there, and it's a great honour. I've had to decide between two courses of action. Either to take legal action against Banting or accept this post, and it's been a very hard decision to reach. My wife and I are very happy here in Canada, and I personally have enjoyed my position here. Had it not been for the distress Banting's behaviour has brought me, I think I would have stayed until I retired, but the university would not benefit by a spectacular court case. If a defamation case was begun, it would involve myself and the man who is held to be a hero of the medical field, so it's quite possible I might not win.'

He drew out the pipe and tobacco pouch, filled the bowl, and lit up.

'Your coffee's as good as always, Stella, and I enjoy a smoke with it.'

Stella nodded again.

'Yes. I know you do...' she said, still softly. Macleod took another sip of liquid.

'There's another matter too. My health's not as good as it used to be. Rheumatoid arthritis is not a thing I can do a lot about. There are pain-reducing treatments, but I'm not keen on becoming too reliant on them. My European tours are becoming increasingly hard, physically, for me to tackle. These will be made easier if my home is in the United Kingdom. I have to tell you, Stella, that my decision is to return to Aberdeen within the next few months. That'll probably be around April or May.'

Stella looked over to Macleod. She saw even more clearly the toll that the past few years had taken. While surprised at the news, she felt that his judgement was right.

'We'll all miss you, Professor, miss you a great deal, but I'd like to thank you for taking me into your confidence in this way, and for your kindness to me, not only to me, but to the many students who've benefited so much from your help and advice. No doubt that may never be recognised, but I feel that it's likely that many would never have made it without your guidance, and that applies particularly to the Insulin team.'

Macleod inclined his head to her and smiled.

'You always say the right thing, Stella. I'm sure you'll do the same for my successor, whoever that may be. Now, can we draft a reply to Aberdeen University?'

Secrets only last a short time in the hothouse atmosphere of a university. Professor Fitzgerald paid Banting a visit soon after JJR's decision.

'Can we talk in your office, Fred? Something I don't think you know about.'

Banting could see that his caller was excited. His first sentence told him the reason.

'Macleod's leaving.'

'What? You're surely not telling me that he's going away for good. D'you mean on another lecture tour?'

'No. Permanently.'

Fred drew a bottle and two glasses from his desk drawer.

'Well... If ever there was a cause for a drink, it's right now.'

Back at Avenue Street, just as Marion found that her husband was not the man she thought he was, Fred found that Marion did not match up with the way he believed a wife should behave either; she was not homeloving like his mother. She did not express much interest in his work; she had lost interest in sexual activity too, at least with her husband, but she told him she was expecting a child. Fred had good reason to feel down, there was even the odd occasion when he hit her.

Marion became involved in work to do with the Girl Guide movement. Fred spent more and more time at the lab, or on nights out with the boys. He forgot her birthday. He did not turn up at all sometimes for dinner. She was left to cry bitter tears alone.

Her baby, christened 'Bill', was born, but even the safe arrival of a son made little difference to Fred's behaviour.

Marion began to be seen regularly with D.M. LeBourdaise, an education director. This man was a friend of a struggling freelance writer, Blodwen Davies, the girl who was spending time with Fred.

Marion spoke to her father about Blodwen.

'She's often invited to dinner at our house. Fred never even phones to tell me. She goes to the upstairs rooms with him, and spends most of the evening up there until late. It's a case of Blodwen here with Fred, Blodwen there with Fred, Blodwen everywhere... with Fred.

I wouldn't mind so much if he wasn't so casual about it. I still live there, after all...'

Her husband took an increasing dislike to 'DM'. For reasons best known to himself, he decided to take steps.

There was a sudden cracking sound one evening as the glass panel in LeBourdaise's front door was smashed. Two private detectives and Fred burst into the apartment. According to their version, both Marion's and DM's clothing was 'disturbed'. Fred grabbed

DM by the throat and forced him over a settee, so far that he fell down the back of it.

'Hold on, Doctor. You can't take a corpse to court,' one of the detectives said.

Later that evening, Marion went to see Sir William Mulock, Chief Justice of Ontario and chancellor of the university. Fred went home to Avenue Street, took his belongings from the house, and also consulted Mulock the next day.

Torontonians and those who were not close friends of the couple had always assumed that the Banting lake was placid. The first the public knew of the storm troubling the waters was an announcement in the *Star*: 'Frederick Banting, MD, formerly of 46 Bedford Road, Toronto, will not be responsible for debts contracted in my name without written consent.'

Telephone lines throughout the city were constantly engaged as soon as the *Star* went on sale. 'Curiosity killed the cat', the saying goes. The curious cat was dead within the hour.

The university's most skilled psychologist, Doctor William Blatz, agreed to act as go-between in divorce proceedings. 'Blow the whole thing wide open', Fred blurted to him.

Blatz, who knew him well, warned him that such an event would damage his reputation irreparably. 'A professor ... at the university ... the hero of Insulin ... disgraced.'

The only comment that dissuaded Fred from blundering on was when Blatz remarked,

'What do you think the university will make of such a thing?'

Sir William Mulock and Blatz persuaded the pair to take their advice.

'If Marion and LeBourdaise don't defend the action, the whole business could be dealt with quietly, in camera, behind closed doors in the Supreme Court. There'll be *no* press reporters there,' said Mulock. 'I'll see to that,' he said, reassuringly.

Marion's custody of the child, an arrangement from Fred to pay maintenance of $250 per month and give her possession of the house, were all agreed amicably enough.

Sir William Mulock undertook to see that the lid was kept on the forthcoming court attendance date, and all looked well for a surgically clean cut from each other, but warnings were already coming from legal friends of the couple that what they were doing was hedged with danger.

Divorce cases were few and far between in Toronto. The applicants were tainted for life thereafter, and collusion to arrange affairs between the disputants was strictly against the law. Acording to new rules applying to divorce, that was a matter for the court.

On the afternoon of 25 April, a decree nisi was granted when no defendants appeared to dispute the evidence of the detectives that Marion Banting and D.M. LeBourdaise had been seen together, intimately together.

Fred and Marion went off quietly through a side door as the next case began. The terms of the decree nisi stated that divorce was to become absolute in six months provided no further evidence came to light.

The whole plan disintegrated when the story appeared on the front page of the *Toronto Telegram* in its evening edition on the day of the hearing.

Because the ageing Chief Justice, Sir William Mulock, had not understood the limits applying to new divorce laws, his assurance that there would be no publicity was quite incorrect. There *had* been a *Telegram* reporter in court, notepad at the ready, breathlessly jotting down names and details of the biggest scoop of his career.

Marion's father, Doctor Alex Robertson, immediately started investigations into Banting's connections with Blodwen Davies. A close friend warned Banting that he should see her 'more discreetly, for the sake of the university'.

Fred answered, 'I'll meet her in the park rather than her

apartment…'

Things went from bad to worse. Doctor Robertson and William LeBourdaise filed an intervention, denying the evidence Banting's men had presented and claiming that collusion had taken place. The media performed in its usual voracious way. The *Star* published every detail of the cases, naming names, describing the most salacious aspects of the scandal.

Readers were utterly astounded. Hollywood stars did this sort of thing, but *never* Frederick Banting, the man who made Canada famous, the man who discovered the lifesaver of the century… never.

BANTING CRUEL TO WIFE and FATHER CLAIMS FAMOUS RESEARCHER'S ASSAULT AGAINST DAUGHTER were but some of the banner headlines.

Sir William Mulock called on the editor of the *Star* to withhold the story, but his plea was rejected out of hand.

Dead or alive, the cat was out of the bag with a vengeance.

'Toronto the Good' as the city was known, was certainly not the place for Professor Banting to try to brassneck his way out of such a situation.

Prominent men involved in divorce were not invited to society affairs, any more than were females, and this divorce was the nastiest in living memory.

'I chose you to partner Marion at dinner dances because you weren't married,' Fred told LeBourdaise. But LeBourdaise *was* married; his wife and he were separated. She lived in California and came back to defend her husband's name and reputation, but he, at the time specified, was having an affair with yet another woman in addition to Marion.

LOTHARIO CARRIES OFF THREE WOMEN SIMULTANEOUSLY, the papers said, having dug up the juiciest bits, as only the press can.

They all got off lightly. The judge ruled that the intervention and collusion charges were not sufficiently proven to justify a new trial. Banting had the university strongly behind him. Even Walter Graham came out to support him, among others such as the staunch old Philatea Club members, but there were a few who thought that the scandal would force his resignation, 'And good riddance too… Nothing but a trouble maker… Thinks he's one of God's chosen…'

Fred did not resign.

Marion had far less support. Some of her 'friends' claimed, 'She's a flirt. If it hadn't been DM it would've been some of her other men friends…'

On 2 December 1932, the decree was declared absolute.

After the case was over, Fred unfolded his views to Duncan Graham, his old enemy who had become sympathetic and understanding.

'What're you going to do now?' Graham asked.

'Well, this has been a helluva business, Duncan. I like sketching, so I'm off on a painting trip, far away, until the storm blows itself out. If I'd my way, I'd put a muzzle on every reporter in sight. Why can't they see the lovely side of life? Democracy in the United States and Canada stinks.'

Marion sold the big house. Her father asked what she intended to do.

'I'm moving to Oakville. It's only a few miles out of Toronto, so I'll be able to come in and see you and my friends. This house is far too big for me alone. The city has too many unhappy memories for me just now. I've got a good job,' she told her father. 'It's in Simpson's departmental store. I'm to be head of the Shopper's Service, where I can do my own thing. Bill's to be looked after during the day at Bill Blatz's experimental school at the university. Fred'll have him at weekends.'

Her father looked relieved. With Marion out of sight, the press would lose interest, and Banting was also going away. The heat should die away.

Banting's journeys took in Boston, where he visited Doctor Joslin's clinic for diabetics at the Deaconess Hospital. Elliot Joslin welcomed him with open arms.

'Delighted to see you, Fred. Come away into my office and meet my new associate, Priscilla White.'

The moment Fred's eyes took in her tall, lithe figure, his mind took off again.

She was twenty-eight; he was over forty.

'How do you do,' he said, taking her hand firmly, so firmly she found it hard to detach herself. 'Very well, thank you,' she murmured.

The relationship developed. He asked her out to dinner one evening at a conference where they met again.

They held hands over the table as Fred asked if she was finding the lectures boring.

'I sure am. Had you something else in mind?'

'Well, how about taking the day off tomorrow? We'll go sleigh riding instead.'

They went sleigh riding…

Priscilla began to feel drawn towards him much more than casually.

'Y'know, Fred, I think the world of you. I've treated diabetic children in Elliot Joslin's wards for years, seen them grow thinner and thinner, fade away until they die, poor little things. You've brought them the means to live, not only live but grow healthy, run about, take an interest in things, like children should… You must feel great about it.'

Fred's heart began to beat faster as he returned her gaze.

When she returned to the clinic, Joslin was waiting for her.

'Priscilla, let me give you some advice. I know Fred Banting's been seeing you a lot lately. I don't like this at all. The man's a divorcee – the last sort of person a caring girl like you should get involved with. I think he's a brilliant man, but his morals are corrupt. I'm asking you to stop seeing him. You'll feel bad, even hurt that I should intervene this way, but my faith prevents me allowing this affair to go on. Will you? Please?'

When Fred phoned her, she refused his invitation to meet again. After several more failed attempts, he gave up.

Back in Toronto, Blodwen tried to contact him after hearing nothing from him during and after the conference. She too worshipped him. The letters she sent showed the depth of her feelings.

3 July 1933

'I have waited for you tonight but you have not come. You have strange ideas about a woman's love. I tried to give you all the sympathy and tenderness when you were unhappy.

'My heart is broken because you are so different to the man I idealised and depended on for affection, for those things that would have made life tolerable and even happy…

'There is nothing more to say but what will cause more pain to each of us…

'Goodbye. I hope some day to be able to think about happier things. I don't know why I should be punished so for the best impulses of my life. Perhaps some day I shall know.

'Please don't try to see me.'
Blodwen

When Fred read the letter he felt bad about it, and went to see Blatz.

'Look, Bill, I got this letter from Blodwen. She sounds pretty low. I don't want to hurt her; we were pretty close friends y'know.'

Blatz looked at Fred intently after scanning through her words.

'You… you weren't so close that she's pregnant, were you?'

Fred coloured up a little.

'Well, I really don't want to talk about it. We were good friends and that's all I want to say about her. D'you think I should see her, try to calm her down?'

'If I were you, I'd go away now – and stay away for a while. Don't see her again. Don't reply to the letters she's sending you. The consequences might be disastrous for you. If you're seen out and about with Blodwen, the papers are sure to get hold of it.

They'll say it proves you were guilty of adultery and they'll try to destroy your character again. This time it probably will.'

'Lucky in war, unlucky in love,' Fred replied.

'How do you mean?'

'I survived the war, didn't I?'

Fred took the advice. Poor Blodwen became another casualty.

CHAPTER 19

1934–1941

A number of events followed the divorce.

There was a 27,000-ton ship, the *Beolithic*, sailing from North Sydney, Nova Scotia, with supplies for ports in Canada's Eastern Arctic, returning with furs and merchandise from the Hudson Bay stations there.

Art was something in which Banting had become deeply interested, so much so that his paintings were displayed in many prominent exhibitions, and received favourable comments from expert critics. The frozen wastes seemed a likely place to find inspiration. He approached officials of the Canadian Department of the Interior to ask if there was a chance of joining the ship as its medical officer. They must have wondered why the discoverer of Insulin wanted such a job, especially as there was already one appointed, but the government decided to allow him to go along as a guest. A.Y. Jackson, a professional artist, had been with Fred on trips before, and joined him on this one. The telegram approving the voyage read, 'If you are prepared to face the hazards of the north and assume responsibility, the Department will be glad to have you. Can offer nothing luxurious.'

They sailed less than a week later.

Charles Best, now established as an active medical researcher, heard about his former colleague's intention with some disdain.

His wife Margaret and he discussed the news. Charley was never much into art.

'He was supposed to be spending the summer in the lab. I suppose they'll paint polar bears, icebergs... and things...'

The officers' mess received the pair with some reservations.

The second mate muttered, under his breath, 'Don't want a

couple of Nancy-boy artists on board a ship like this.'

The captain was also unsure of how to treat them. 'You'll not find things on the *Beolithic* much like the kind of luxury you get on the liners you've travelled over the Atlantic in, Doctor Banting.' Inwardly he wondered if 'Professor' was the proper way to address him, or maybe Mister. His listener made no comment, so everyone settled for 'Doctor'.

'We're not hard to please, Captain. Your men have important work to do, and we'll not get in their way.'

That seemed to satisfy the skipper, and he poured a generous amount of rum into their glasses. 'Here's to success, then. Cheers!'

The trip was boring after the first couple of weeks. Endless ploughing through broken icebergs floating in dull grey seas, stops at small outposts, Pond Inlet, Clyde, Pangnirtung and Lake Harbour. Few were of interest to anyone except the crew, but the two artists were able to complete some good paintings. The only semi-exciting episode was when the ship almost became trapped in ice at Bache, then failed to reach Melville Island, south-east of Ellesmere. They were storm-bound at Beechey Island, where the litter of several Arctic expeditions had been left.

Wandering along the debris-strewn beach one day, Fred found a whisky bottle lodged in stones above the waterline. It was a relic – the ship captain's idea – of the 1922 Canadian Arctic expedition.

Contained inside was a paper giving the names of those who had been members. Banting and Jackson added theirs, and replaced the bottle.

The trip to Alaska produced another Banting outburst, this time one that landed him in serious trouble.

The *Toronto Star* journalist who was waiting to interview the two men as the *Beolithic* docked was none other than Fred Greenaway. The subject discussed with them on the long train journey back to Toronto was about art, the voyage and the people they met.

Fred had given a promise to the Ministry of the Interior that he would not make any comment to the press, but looked through the reporter's notes carefully.

'That's fine,' he remarked to Greenaway. 'Y'can send that off; it's OK. Come along to my carriage and we'll have a drink. I've got a couple of bottles of rum the captain gave me as a parting present.'

They had a great deal to drink and the rum was potent stuff, but Greenaway had far less than Fred. When Banting began to talk about how the Hudson Bay Company treated the Eskimos, Greenaway realised he was on to another story as Fred rambled on in his own inimitable way.

* * *

The day Banting came back to the university, there was a phone call from the Deputy Minister of the Interior.

'Professor Banting, I have to ask what statements you have been giving the press about the Alaska trip. You were seen talking to reporters on the journey. You gave an undertaking that you would refrain from any contact with the media.'

'That's right. There was a reporter with Jackson and me on the train journey back, but I vetted his notes. They were totally inoffensive, and covered the art side of the voyage only. After all, we had quite a lot to tell him.'

'Have you seen today's *Star*, Professor?'

Fred had not.

'I suggest you go out and buy one,' the Minister said dryly.

Fred flushed as he spread the paper out. His name headed the front page:

BANTING REGRETS HUDSON BAY USE OF ESKIMOS

Word for word, remarks Fred had made to the reporter were quoted.

'The Hudson Bay Company is conning the Eskimos … They give beads and cheap baubles for thousands of dollars worth of furs. … The natives would be far better off as they were before capitalism overtook them. The profit from furs in other countries [he meant Denmark] is administered by the government. The money is used to help the natives by persuading them to improve their diet, eat food that is better for them … advance their lot. There is scarcely a real Canadian among the English and Scotsmen in the Hudson Bay Company…'

It was an ill-advised article attacking one of Canada's greatest business achievements. The hot-tempered delegation of enraged Hudson Bay governors, who sought an immediate meeting, was after Banting's blood.

A red-faced Banting defended himself by saying that the discussions with Greenaway had covered the *Beolithic* trip, what they had been painting, and the people and the places where they had dropped anchor.

'I checked his notes and I didn't make any report to the Department of the Interior. They were paying all my expenses after all… I felt the subject so unimportant. These remarks the *Star* feature included were just talk and off the cuff. I was certain that their journalist and I *had* been having an informal chat, not for publication.'

The interview ended with the Hudson Bay men departing far from satisfied.

A minority wanted to sue Banting for defamation, but were eventually overruled.

Greenaway called at Banting's house in an effort to sort things out. He got no further than the front door.

'You've got some nerve coming here! I'll have you fired!' Banting fumed, before slamming the door in Greenaway's face. He was not to speak to the reporter again for over ten years.

Banting learned yet again that the 'off-the-cuff' comment is the very meat the ever-voracious media looks for.

* * *

It was 1934, and moves were being made in London to make up the King's birthday honours list.

An envelope was waiting in his office when Banting came back to Toronto. The people at the benches in the Medical Research Department building greeted Fred cheerfully as he passed through.

They were a mixed bunch. Some were genuine researchers trying out worthwhile work with the assistance of the fine equipment that the department provided. Professor Banting helped some of the less well off financially, but many were really living cheaply at the university, onto a good thing until their projects were found to be useless.

The important thing to Fred was that they were a sociable lot, liked a pint or two, knew where to get it, and sang good songs with him when they got a bit oiled up.

The heat was off over the divorce affair. Fred Banting, to most, was one of the boys. If he wanted to play around with the girls, well, why not? So they greeted him cheerfully the day he came back from the Arctic trip.

'Coming out tonight, Fred?' was the invitation on the lips of several.

'Let me see what's in the mail, then I'll be out to see what you've been getting up to while I've been away,' he replied.

The particular envelope that caught his eye was of thick, creamy paper and carried the government insignia on the flap. He opened it first, drew out the letter and began to read.

'My God!'

Sadie Gairns looked up from her desk in the outer office as Fred walked towards her, holding the page out. 'I'm to receive a title!' She took it from him.

'Oh, Fred! Isn't that wonderful? There hasn't been a title granted in Canada for decades.' Her eyes moistened as she read it; she looked at him admiringly.

'You're invited to attend the ceremony, where the Prime Minister'll award the title: "Knight Commander of the Civil Division of the Order of the British Empire". Sounds a bit cumbersome, but you'll be *Sir* Frederick after that. I used to have a picture book when I was little that had a "Sir Frederick" in it. He looked marvellous in shiny armour and sitting on a white horse. You'd look good on one too, Fred, come to think of it.'

'Not on your life, Sadie. I doubt if I'll ever use the title and I don't want any fuss made over it, but you'd better join the party that the boys outside'll want once they hear about this.'

It was a pretty wild party. The amount of drink Fred consumed meant he had to be driven home in a taxi. As he left, he remarked to no one in particular, 'The next guy who calls me "Sir" get his ass kicked...'

Although there could never have been a titled fellow more unpretentious than Fred, 'Sir Frederick Grant Banting' looked good at the head of programmes, dinner guest lists, lectures, speeches and social events.

In the laboratory, Professor Banting decided to embark on another series of experiments, seeking a repeat of the Insulin standard, but none proved successful.

Restless and stressed, he decided to get clear of Toronto.

'Sadie, I've often wanted to go to Russia. Could you make enquiries for me? Make the necessary bookings – maybe by train through France and Germany?'

In Russia he met the 85-year-old Pavlov, Russia's famed scientist and physiologist.

'He was not the quiet, studious man I had pictured,' he said to the scientists at the Research Department when he came back.

'He talked non-stop in the most animated way, in Russian of course, to his party of visitors who sat in a half-circle. They obviously worshipped him. We could do with taking a leaf out of the Russian leadership's book.' Stalin was the leader.

Banting's party of Europeans had been taken on a carefully conducted tour, where nothing was in evidence of the slaughter which had followed the 1917 revolution and was still going on, nor of the abject misery that Stalin's regime was inflicting on its defenceless citizens at the time.

Fred Banting fell for the convincing political stories put forward, backed by visits to schools and hospitals, which were models of advanced thinking.

'I'm convinced that communism is the key to world peace,' he declared once back in Toronto to the newspapers and his circle of friends, Fred Hipwell, and those former pupils of his teenage school days, Class IT7.

Invited to dinner at the house of the Governor-General of Ontario, he suddenly stood up and announced 'I **am** a communist!'

* * *

Things were not going well for Professor Banting. The buildings, hospital wards, clinics and lecture halls to which his name was applied, such as the Banting and Best Chair of Medical Research, awards such as the Apothecaries Medal of the Ancient Society of Apothecaries in London, the Flavelle Medal of the Royal Society of Canada and Fellowship of the Royal College of Surgeons – the list was endless.

It would have delighted most men, but the experiments he was undertaking at the Banting Research Institute were not meeting with success.

Now that he had every facility to delve into whatever 'idea' came up in his research department, a guilt complex assailed him. His cousin Fred Hipwell had been a confidante since the boyhood days in Alliston, and Banting always felt calmer after a talk with him. Calling to see him, he described how unhappy he felt.

'I feel bad about the way people ask what experiment I'm doing at present. I can't tell them because few are turning out well. Reporters keep calling at the Institute, the office, my home, even on my friends. The press said I was on the brink of something a while ago, and although I refused to give details on it, the next issue's front page hinted at another tremendous event like the Insulin one, not connected with it, but equally dramatic.

'It finished up with hundreds of poor, sick people turning up at the medical building, queuing up, waiting to see me. I was actually working on a type of cancer at the time, but the project didn't lead anywhere.

'I had to publish a denial and asked that it be printed exactly as I wrote it, but this too was altered to say that there *was* something in the wind, but more work needed to be done.'

Hipwell poured whisky into his glass, and topped up Fred's.

'Y'know, your biggest enemies have always been the newsmen. It's very fine to have a Free Press, but we've all seen the results of such freedom. You'd have been better staying away from them.'

Fred took a gulp of his drink. 'D'you not think I've tried? Leaving by side doors at hotels and lecture halls, not answering the door at home, not speaking on the telephone. I can manage to stay away from *them*. It's they who won't stay away from *me*…'

Hipwell looked reflectively through the glass in his hand at the fire flickering in the grate before draining it.

'It's the price you have to pay for being famous, Fred. I'll have to go. I've a pile of case notes to write up. Can I see you at the Bloor Street office tomorrow? There are one or two patients I'd like to discuss with you.'

'Any time. The afternoon OK?'

He left cousin Hipwell with a parting remark, 'The more I think of the city, the more I want to live in the country, and the more I think of being a professor of research, the more I want to be an artist.'

The next day, Hipwell talked over the cases with Banting at the Bloor Street practice.

Once finished, the smell of ground coffee percolating through the rooms made them relax and enjoy a chat over cups of it. Fred Banting lit his usual cigarette.

'What's on the cards at the lab just now, Fred?' Hipwell asked.

'You know I've been dabbling in a possible treatment for Rous Sarcoma? Sadie's kept busy transplanting cancerous tumours into chickens – about three hundred so far.' Hipwell was puzzled. 'What's that for?' he asked.

His heart sank at his cousin's next remark.

'It's an "idea" I have…'

For several years, Banting's experiments involving such treatment led to the deaths of some 1,768 birds and no progress towards a cure for cancer.

He was not alone in this avenue, any more than others had been in the case of Insulin, but the investigators of the 1930s were up against an incredibly complex illness.

Better results came Banting's way when research began into silicosis, an illness common in the many mining communities in Canada. The Ontario Mining Association prompted him to see what could be done about it. Much of the work done in the Banting Research Department was by others, and few of their papers had his name heading them, but all the suggested treatments for the serious problem were well received by the authorities.

The press once more suddenly launched into details of a success by Professor Sir Frederick Banting, and telegrams, cards and letters of congratulation poured into the university and his home. He was away on one of his European tours at the time. In fact, the man who was making progress into the lung disease was another cancer researcher, William Franks.

He had developed an 'idea' of his own that silica dust could be removed from the atmosphere, after blasting operations, by electrical precipitation.

His machine to do this was ready for field testing when his wife gave birth to twins, and he suspended operations for a time.

He was surprised to read that such a machine, 'invented by Professor Banting at Toronto University' had already been successful! Fred Banting had had nothing to do with such a device and was equally surprised at the news.

Fred Hipwell was right about the press, and Bill Franks's machine failed anyway.

* * *

Once home from a conference in France some time later, he called Sadie into his office.

'I've had a letter from the Canadian Research Council asking me to become a member. Feeling as I do, that there's another war coming, I could contribute something to it. Could you take down a reply, giving my acceptance please?'

She fetched her notebook and prepared to jot down his comments, knowing that once they were noted, she would type the letter in her own words later. Fred' grammar was still atrocious.

'Who do I reply to?' Sadie asked.

Fred handed the letter to her. 'The heading's on that, with the address. General Andrew G.I. McNaughton is the president. He's quite a guy – I remember his name cropping up during the last war. He's an engineer, an artillery man, inventor and a scientist. There was an item in the papers recently that he managed to get a $400,000 annual grant out of the government and he's out to get more to expand the activities of the CRC. I think I'll enjoy working with him.'

By 1938, the Council had been renamed as 'The Associate Committee on Medical Research', and Professor Banting was chairman. The post was more of an administrative nature, and apart from the preparation of reports about his belief that chemical warfare would almost certainly be used in the nearing conflict, he was to make more speeches on the Insulin breakthrough than ever before.

General McNaughton sent for him one day.

'I'd like you to visit as many universities and hospitals, provincial public health laboratories and the like in Canada. Find out just what research they're all doing. It'll be quite a bit of work, but I know you'll do it well.'

'Do you think they may be duplicating the work we're doing here?' Banting asked.

'Well, nowadays, research is expensive, very expensive, and there's so much to do. Maybe we could farm some out to them and save money in the process. It's a duty for Canada, is the research business.'

'Of course I'll do it, Sir.' If he had added 'For King and Country', it would not have been out of place. His face was flushed with patriotic enthusiasm.

Hopes that he might get away from the subject of Insulin didn't materialise. Everywhere he went, speeches *were* expected. Platform speaking was something he had never been good at or comfortable performing. He had neither a Velyian Henderson nor a Sadie Gairns at his side to ghost-write them.

There was the occasional break, such as when he called at the McGill University in Montreal. James Collip, formerly Professor of Physiology at Alberta, the man who had successfully refined the unreliable extracts produced in the 1922 days, welcomed him.

He had been appointed Professor of Biology at the McGill in 1928. The animosity that had broken out after the Nobel award had long since dispersed, and they had become the best of friends.

'My dear Fred,' Collip said. 'Come away into the office. You'll come home with me and have dinner afterwards. My wife'll be so pleased to see you. I'll phone right now and tell her you're coming.'

After the meal, the two men went to James's study, to talk and reminisce.

'You've got married again, Fred, Collip remarked as he refilled Fred's whisky glass.

'Yes. It's been quite a year, 1939,' he remarked. 'Good health, James.' The glasses clinked cheerfully together. 'Well? Come on, tell me about it.'

Fred dug out his packet of cigarettes. James shook his head when asked if he minded smoking. He noticed the rasping cough that Fred had developed when they worked together in Toronto in 1922 was worse; much worse. 'Not at all. Some of my own family smoke, though I never started.'

Fred drew smoke into his lungs before beginning to reply. The alcohol was beginning to loosen his tongue.

'Maybe I'd have done better marrying Edith in the first place. She was so patient for so long, and I really thought the world of her. In the early days, when our research started, it was terrible to have no money, no gifts I could afford for her birthdays or meals out, yet she still wanted to be my wife. It must have been hard for her to understand that I couldn't let her pay for everything. She's married now, happily as far as I know. Marriage to Marion was doomed from the start. We were poles apart, and the divorce was absolutely terrible. I had to go away, far away. I went on a painting trip to Alaska on a survey ship.

'I *had* to get free of the press, and it was years before I could suffer the sight of Ted Greenaway, the *Star* reporter. What he said about my thoughts on the Hudson Bay behaviour landed me in deep trouble.'

Collip remembered the press reports very well. Fred took a drink before carrying on.

'And now there's Henrietta Ball, the girl I married last year. She was twenty-seven then, studying for an MA degree at Toronto University. She came to my department two years before that, part time, and of course, we met quite a lot there. The Hipwells were the only ones who knew about our stepping out together. We used to meet at their house, drive out of town, and have dinner somewhere well off the beaten track.'

'This was to avoid being followed by reporters?' James suggested.

'Too bloody true! They stop at nothing, these people. Anyway, she and I couldn't agree about getting together before marriage, and she went off to London to see friends. Neither the Hipwells nor Sadie Gairns thought marrying her was a good idea, but I didn't agree, so I went after her to England.

'We booked into a small hotel in London as man and wife for a few nights, and there was no doubt about it after that... She's a lovely girl. We wed a year later, and we're sublimely happy. Sadie Gairns threatened to leave the department if I married her, but she's still with me.'

'And what about your son: Bill?'

'He's nine now. "Henrie" – that's what the Hipwells nicknamed Henrietta so's people who might hear the name in conversation wouldn't realise that "Henrie" was a girl – took to him straight off and everything's fine there, thank goodness. Sees his mother every week though.'

'No family by "Henrie" then?' prompted Collip, filling the glasses.

'No. Not yet. But I dearly want to have a family, lots of little girls as well as boys...'

James listened patiently to Fred's story. He understood the difficulties Fred had suffered during the early days in the hot, smelly rooms given them by Macleod, but he had never agreed with Banting's views of the professor. He did not raise the topic of Macleod's death in 1935 at his home in Aberdeen, just seven years after his departure from Toronto.

* * *

The next matter that Banting began to study was the effect altitude had on the lungs of pilots flying at ever-greater levels. Low oxygen, low air pressure and the centifrugal force exerted on the body at high speed turns could do damage if steps were not taken.

He consulted General McNaughton.

'I think we should establish a research committee to look into these matters. The kind of planes that will be used in warfare will be capable of speeds never thought possible just a few years ago,' Banting proposed.

His plan led to the formation of the Aviation Medical Research Committee. Its first meeting was on 7 June 1939, with a budget of $16000.

When the meetings between British Prime Minister Neville Chamberlain and German Chancellor Adolf Hitler failed when Czechoslovakia was invaded, war was declared. Professor Banting called his staff to a meeting in his department.

'I do not think you should join the armed forces,' he declared. 'The services of skilled scientists and research people will be of more value to the war effort here. Do not feel that there is any compulsion to remain here, but that is definitely my advice,' he announced, stepping down off the podium from where he had addressed them. Next, he went to his office, took off his white coat, and drove down to the enlisting office. There, he offered his services to the Canadian Army. He was given a commission at once.

There were no uniforms that would fit, and some delay was envisaged in delivery. Fred went to cousin Hipwell next. He knew that both his and Frederick's First World War outfits were still in a wardrobe.

'Go and fetch my old uniform for me please. I'll just wear that until my new one comes.'

CHAPTER 20

1941
February

Major Sir Frederick Grant Banting was suffering from stress – something that had plagued him many times before, and from which he had to make his escape.

Considering the continuing insistence by the Canadian press that he was a genius, there should have been little reason for his being downcast.

The official reason for the London trip was to confer with other British scientific pundits over his obsession that chemical warfare would be carried out by the Germans.

The real reason may have been that he simply wanted to see old British Army pals again, get a little drunk with them, and wallow in memories about the First World War that they all recalled so vividly.

It was on Saturday, 15 February 1941, that the message came to his Toronto office instructing him to report at Montreal's St Hubert Airfield next morning for the trip to England.

Sadie Gairns was almost tearful. She was the only member of the university staff to be against the London visit.

'Once you're there, they'll probably not let you come back. You've plenty to do here, y'know.'

Looking at her, smiling a little, he put a hand on her arm.

'Don't worry, Sadie. I couldn't stay away very long from you.'

She looked at him quizzically, accustomed to his flippancy. 'Come on now! I know you make passes at all the girls! Anyway, you've got a wife, and she wouldn't approve.'

She picked up some letters and made to leave.

'Hold on a minute, Sadie. Speaking of my wife, Henrietta and my son Bill are coming to see me off at the station. Could you give them a cup of coffee when they arrive? I'd be grateful for that.'

Sadie told him she would go and set a tray for them.

She reappeared a little later with a bundle of files.

'These are the papers you asked me to put together for the conferences in London. I think you'll find them all in order.'

Fred squared them up on the desk and pushed them into a holdall.

'Thanks. I'm sure they will be.' He put the case on the floor beside a leather briefcase.

Sadie Gairns had acted as a mother figure to Fred in many ways over the years, soothing him when bad temper made him fly off the handle, encouraging him when things looked promising.

At nearly fifty, he was still good looking; a little stooped perhaps, a bit more horse-faced as he got older, but a smiler with a twinkle in his eye. He was something of a Lothario as far as the staff at the hospital was concerned. They were easy prey because of his fame and reputation.

Henrietta and her eleven-year-old stepson Bill came to the Banting and Best laboratories later that morning. Sadie took Henrietta to her own office and sent Bill through to Banting's room. Explaining that the boy's father wanted a word with him on his own, she asked Henrietta if she would like a coffee.

'Yes thanks,' she nodded. 'Pour one for yourself, Sadie.'

The two chatted about the London journey, how the war was going – badly for Britain at the time – and what effect it was having on Canada.

Bill walked into the room where his father was waiting for him.

'Shut the door and come and sit here,' he told the boy, pulling a chair close to the desk.

'I'm flying to England tomorrow. The plane from Montreal takes me to Gander airfield. That's in Newfoundland. Then it's to London for a round of very dull talks about the possibility of germ warfare and what we might do about it.'

'The plane flies over the Atlantic, doesn't it?' his son enquired. 'What'll you do if it comes down in the sea?'

'Don't think about things like that. Planes are crossing the water every day now; there's nothing special about that,' he assured the boy.

'I'm sure you can survive as long as anyone can, even in the cold,' Bill told him.

Why had the boy raised such a point, Fred wondered uneasily.

'I just wanted to have a chat with you before I go. You're the man in the family when I'm not there, so I want you to promise that you'll look after your mother *and* your stepmother until I get back. You will, won't you?'

Bill fixed his eyes on his father's. 'Of course I will. I promise.'

Fred hugged the boy for a moment, then drew back.

'That's fine. Now you can give me a help to get these cases to the hall downstairs.'

'I'll take this one,' Bill offered, trying to lift the briefcase. It was so heavy that he had to use both hands.

'What've you got in this, Dad?'

'It's my diaries, Bill. I write up all the things that've happened during the day, usually just before going to bed. I've done it ever since I was at school. I don't know why I carry them all, now that they're getting so heavy. Just a habit, I think, but sometimes I need to refer to things that happened long ago. Maybe in a year or two, I'll put some in a bookcase at home as even I won't be able to lift them. Why not start keeping a record like that yourself?'

Pulling the desk drawer open, he took a handsomely bound leather book from it.

'Look, here's a new diary for next year. I'll have a look at it once you've started, and keep you right about how to write it up.'

The pair took a handle each of the briefcase between them, with the holdall in Banting's free hand, and made their way to the lift. Henrietta and Sadie joined them at the hallway below. Fred's father and mother arrived, along with another couple – cousin Frederick, and Lillian Hipwell.

Fred welcomed them and suggested that they all come to the station. Sadie did not go, giving Banting a slightly emotional farewell; the others packed themselves into taxis.

'Managed to tear yourself away from the farm then?' Fred asked his father, who was sitting beside him. 'Yeah. Your mother wanted that we see you off.'

There was a short silence, then William spoke again. 'Are these planes safe for such long trips? They tell me that long-distance tanks are fitted for flights over the Atlantic. The extra weight must make take-off a bit difficult, does it not? Especially with passengers on board'

The questions were making Fred uncomfortable. Not being well up in aircraft design, he didn't really know enough to answer the questions. He muttered something about his father knowing more about aircraft than he did himself, lapsed into silence, and concentrated on looking out of the window.

The Montreal station was busy, the platforms being crowded with servicemen and civilians.

A whistle blew, steam jetted from the giant engine, and carriage doors began to slam. Henrietta hugged her husband, and they kissed passionately. The others shuffled their feet, embarrassed at the parting so highly charged with emotion, until Fred drew away.

'Right then, I gotta go,' he said, swinging his luggage up into the carriage. Shutting the door, he leant out of the open window and kissed his mother, then shook hands with the Hipwells and young Bill. Just with that, the train began to move. The party watched him wave until the train curved away out of sight.

Arriving safely at Montreal on Sunday, Banting booked into his hotel. Such a short stay did not justify unpacking, so, taking only pyjamas and shaving kit from the case, he stowed the rest away. Sitting down on the bed, he checked through the papers Sadie had given him. She had done her job well – as usual. All were in order.

Freshening up and brushing his uniform, he went down to the bar to see if there might be some airline personnel there.

Leaning over the bar was a tall man wearing the uniform of the Canadian TransPacific Airline. The insignia showed him to be a radio operator. He straightened up when he saw the major approach.

'My name's Banting – Fred Banting.'

The radioman took in the red pips on the shoulders of the army uniform, and the medal ribbons on the left breast.

'Hi there! My surname's Tripp, but they call me by my initials – CM.'

He gave a warm smile and extended his hand. Banting bought him a drink and asked what was going on at the airfield.

'I'm on regular flights over "The Big Pond" to England, on board the bombers we're delivering to help the war effort. The British are having a rough time with the Luftwaffe bombing London, and have heavy civilian casualties. Hopefully these American-built planes will be over Berlin giving the Jerries some of their own medicine as soon as we can get them there. I've made about twelve trips so far.

'We're sort of stuck just now, as the weather has closed most of the airfields in Newfoundland. That's where we leave from – from Gander – but it'll likely be shut for a few days. It always happens at this time of year. I think there's a storm brewing right now, so we'll stay here, or fly to Gander and wait there.'

'Call me Fred. I'm going to England too. In a Lockheed Hudson. The pilot is Joe Mackey. Do you know him?'

'Yeah, sure I do. He's good. He was a performance pilot before the war, and can sure handle a plane. I've seen him make the crowds gasp when he did barnstorming shows with a girl perched on the wing of his biplane. We fly in groups of five. You'll likely be along-side us when we eventually leave.'

Banting was reassured. Here was someone who could tell him all about the journey.

'I've heard that this way of getting planes to England is some-thing new. Is that right?'

CM looked thoughtful. 'This business of flying them rather than shipping them's something new for us, right enough, but Joe's done it several times, although he's not keen on having the new oil cool-ers fitted at Gander, they're not reliable in cold weather, and some sabotage is rumoured too. We're all civilian air crew – we work for Canadian TransPacific – and for some, it's their first experience of crossing the Atlantic in twin-engined planes like these. Extra fuel tanks have to be fitted, and that makes flying them a bit heavy until the fuel's used up, but there's no other way of doing it.'

Banting cheered up at the thought that other planes would be in sight of theirs, ready to help if need be. He did not realise that the others would have to fly on if anything went wrong. Apart from giving a position, there was little they could do.

CM gathered some papers he had in a folder on the bar.

'Need to go now, Fred. I'll see you in the morning. Sleep well. By the way, try to get a pair of gloves. It can be pretty cold for pas-sengers on a Hudson.'

Fred stayed at the bar and bought another drink. He was thinking over all the points Tripp had made. There was a long, cold flight ahead. Should he really make the journey? Was this the time of year to do it? How much risk was there?

There was a tap on his shoulder.

'Hi there, Fred! Just called in to wish you "bon voyage".' He turned to find a well-built man there. It was James Collip. His arrival was a delightful surprise

'Well, well. I'm glad to see you,' Banting said. The two began to reminisce again about the old days, talk about the vast improvements made in Insulin, who Fred would meet in London…

'D'you know, I still get letters from people telling me how Insulin is such wonderful stuff, how their lives were transformed, how they enjoy life,' Fred remarked.

Over another drink, the subject turned to the coming flight. Fred started putting his anxieties into words.

'My father thinks it's a sort of guinea pig run. There have been very few passengers taken over during winter. Some of these planes have crashed, and I don't think I'd last long if ours come down in the Atlantic.'

Collip tried to take his friend's mind off the subject.

'There's bound to be survival kits on board, inflatable dinghies. Flares and radio too. The pilot'll be skilled, and so will the crew. I'll see you back here in a few weeks, and I'll look after your work with the National Research Council while you're away, so you've nothing to worry about. I'd better go now – You'll need a rest before tomorrow morning. Take-off might be early.'

Fred went to the door with him and they shook hands.

'By the way James, do you think you could get me a pair of gloves and leave them at the desk? I was told to bring a pair because the temperature in the plane will be low.'

Collip had pulled on his heavy coat and reached into the pocket.

'Here you are, Fred, take mine. They're fur lined and just what you need.'

He thrust them into Fred's hand, and set off with a wave.

Monday, 17 February was a cold morning. Fred was alone at the breakfast table, drinking coffee, smoking and reading the morning paper.

A man came to his table and pulled a chair out, facing him.

'Joe Mackey. I'm the pilot you're flying with.' He stretched a hand across to the major.

'Hi there. Fred Banting. Pleased to meet you. There's coffee in the pot there. Would you like some?'

Joe shook his head.

'I'd like to, but there're things I have to do. I just wanted to let you know we'll be flying out at 8.00 a.m. Could you be out on the airstrip prompt? Do you need a help with luggage?'

Fred shook his head. 'I'm glad to hear that, and, thanks, I can manage my stuff OK'.

T9449 took off from St Hubert's Field; the flight to Gander was to take five hours.

On board was a crew of three: Joe Mackey: radioman Snailham: and William Bird, navigator.

Snailham was sitting in the co-pilot's seat an hour later. Above the roar of the twin engines, he had to shout to Joe.

'Will I bring Major Banting up here? It'll let an an army man see what flying's like.'

Joe shook his head vigorously. 'No. You know I don't like passengers. The trip's risky enough without them. I don't want toffee-nosed army men sitting beside me just now. There's hot coffee in the flasks back there. See if he wants one.'

Banting was finding the cold less severe than he thought it might be. He was able to talk a little with the other two flyers, and learned something of their civilian lives. The three shared the coffee, and he fell asleep in his seat. He woke as Snailham shook his arm.

'We're nearly there. You'll be able to see the airfield from the window.'

The plane tilted sharply and lost height as Joe squared up to the floodlit landing strip. Banting could see several Hudson bombers lined up alongside it. There was snow everywhere around the airfield. Apart from hangars, a control tower and some railway wagons, the place looked pretty desolate. The lights of Gander itself glittered a short distance away. Bird was sitting behind, and leant forward.

Pointing down at the other planes, he said 'They landed yesterday. The four of them'll fly off with us as soon as we get decent weather.'

Banting nodded.

Joe Mackey's expertise brought the bomber down with a three-point landing. As soon as it stopped moving, Snailham lowered a ladder from a hatch beneath the fuselage. A chill draught came through the exit as Bird climbed down, followed by Banting and the others.

He carried the briefcase only; the other kits were to be brought down by orderlies and taken to their quarters.

It was only a short distance to the airport buildings, but Banting had to clench his teeth against the icy cold before reaching them. The wave of heat inside was welcome, and the first person to welcome him was CM.

'Come with me, and I'll take you to your hotel. All the aircrews stay there, and you'll be in good company.'

Several days passed without respite from the howling gale that isolated the place against any flights – either out or in. While aircrews, engineers and medical staff from Gander Hospital spent time talking, smoking, drinking and sleeping, they had little interest in the solitary army man. Banting spent some of the time entering the current diary with all the details of the flight and his impressions of the people encountered, Collip's unexpected call, and the ferocity of the storm that was battering the hotel walls.

CM organised a visit to the Royal Canadian Rifles at their barracks near Gander.

Introducing him as 'Major Frederick Bantings' to the CO. The officer stared at him.

'Not *the* Banting – the Insulin man?' he asked.

Banting nodded. Standing straight, his voice raised, he announced 'Gentlemen! This is Major Sir Frederick Banting. If you know anyone with diabetes, his Insulin will be keeping them alive!'

They were in a crowded mess – a big room. Every man got to his feet and came to attention. A round of applause folllowed.

It was only then that Tripp realised who his new friend was, as the name Banting meant nothing to him and Fred had never mentioned his position in medicine.

Later in the day, CM sought out Joe Mackey. 'Listen! Do you know who the 'Old Gent' as you call him, is?

Joe was even more puzzled as the radioman explained.

'What's a guy of *his* importance doing on a half-crazed trip like this? The Americans have been delivering planes to England via the Azores for months. He'd have been far safer going that way.'

Neither could figure this out other than that some halfwit flight planner had probably slipped up, perhaps, like themselves, not realising who 'Major Banting' was.

The storm blew on, keeping all the airfields in both Newfoundland and New Brunswick shut down. Banting was kept busy, lunching with the army officer and then going on an invited visit to Gander Hospital. Filling in the diary, Banting wrote, 'Trying to get away from medical matters in Toronto, I'm even more involved here in Gander!'

The last event was a party at the hotel that night. It was a wild one, with plenty of alcohol and a trainload of girls imported for the occasion. Joe was well oiled during the evening, and so, for that matter, was Banting. Fred met him the next morning at the breakfast table. The wind was no longer rattling the windows.

'Hey, you're quite a drinker, Fred!' Joe commented. Banting had obviously risen in his estimation after the gathering of the previous night. Banting felt he knew Joe well enough to ask a favour.

'I'm sorry to ask this, but I think I've got a urinary infection. I need to visit the toilet pretty often....'

Joe looked at him quizzically. 'This, after last night's fun, eh? Well... just go as little as you can. I'm the only one allowed to make a mess on the floor. The toilet in the Lockheed Hudson is well back in the tail and when in use, the trim needs adjustment, something pilots dislike.'

Joe turned to leave.

'We'll get away tomorrow. The forecasters are promising good weather.'

The urinary problem was solved by CM later.

'Have some of these,' he said, handing over a cardboard box.

'These' turned out to be pint-sized glass containers with screw-down lids. The label on the box read 'Aircrew, for the use of...'

Fred accepted them gratefully.

CHAPTER 21

1941
Thursday 20th February, 7.50 p.m.
Gander Airport
Dark

After the engines had warmed up, the planes lumbered over the tarmac, moving into position for take-off. Minutes later all five were in the air, all in sight of each other, flying in the same formation, like geese. Similar to all big birds, they were clumsy on the ground, graceful in the sky.

T9449 was out on the port side of the leading craft, T9450. Each had a crew of two and pilot. Joe's was the only plane with a passenger: Fred Banting.

Fifty miles out from the coast, over the Atlantic, Joe saw the plane ahead peeling off in a slow turn, heading back towards Newfoundland. Radioman Snailham heard a message crackle in his headset.

'Hello, you guys. T9450 here. Got engine trouble. Will make Gander OK. See you after the war. Over.'

Ten minutes later, Joe sensed a change in the sound of one of their engines. The oil temperature gauge needle for the starboard engine was moving up through the red band. He stopped the engine and feathered the propeller, preventing the drag that would have been caused by stationary blades.

William Bird, the navigator, appeared beside him, having seen there was a problem. The pilot pointed a gloved hand towards the engine. No explanation was needed.

'Jettison all the movable goods on board, the extra fuel too,' he shouted over the noise.

'Ask Snailham to radio Gander. Ask for a route for going back. Tell them one engine's out. Get the others to put parachutes on and be ready when I give the order.'

The navigator disappeared from the flight deck.

Joe knew that the plane could fly on one engine, but the Hudson would not glide well. Everything depended on the remaining engine. Keeping a close eye on the dials in front of him, he adjusted the trim and turned back towards the airfield.

Soon the Newfoundland shoreline could just be seen below, with white waves marking it. Snailham came forward to the seat beside Joe, confirming that his orders had been carried out. He watched anxiously as the pilot struggled to hold the craft level. Joe leant over to him.

'Tell the others to bail out. We're over land again, but they'll have to go right now. We're losing height fast and at 2500 feet, there's not much time left.'

The radioman nodded and turned away.

Suddenly, there was a bang from the remaining engine, and a wisp of smoke streamed from the casing. Joe became tense as he shut it down.

Immediately, the plane's downward angle increased and speed began to build up.

'We're sure not gonna make Gander,' Joe thought, the altimeter showing height lessening by the second. Snailham reappeared, holding on to the back of the seat as the incline increased.

Joe shouted to him above the mounting vibration from the airframe.

'Are they away?' He meant the navigator and Banting. Snailham shook his head.

'Hell! The others need to brace themselves against anything solid. Face backward. We'll crash in a few minutes. Tell them.'

Snailham had a struggle to get himself out of the flight deck because the floor was now sloping so steeply, but made it.

While stunt flying had been Joe's occupation in peace time, it was going to tax his skill to the utmost to bring his craft safely to the ground. The strumming sound grew to a scream and Joe stared out of the windscreen, wrenching at the joystick, willing the plane to stay aloft long enough to find a place to land, and desperately looking for a lake.

The terrain was now clearly visible, trees everywhere, snow covering the few patches of clear ground, none long enough to land.

Time ran out. Feathery treetops flicked the undercarriage, and then a tall fir gouged a huge piece out of a wing. The plane swivelled round violently, and any chance of a controlled landing was lost. The plane hit the ground.

'This is it!' Joe shouted above the din as the fuselage ploughed along, throwing up snow like white net curtains over the windscreen.

There was a deafening, tearing sound as an outcrop of jagged rocks brought T9449 to a jarring halt.

Joe lost consciousness as something struck his forehead.

The first feeling before opening his eyes was of pain. A few seconds were enough to verify that he was not seriously injured. There was blood on his head, but fire was his main concern. Apart from the creaking sound of hot metal cooling, there were no flames and the plane was upright, impaled on the rocks. Levering himself out of the seat, he staggered back to the main cabin. Through the windows filtered pale shafts of the moon. They lit a ghastly scene. The pilot could see that Snailham and Bird were dead, their open eyes reflecting the moonlight.

A silvery, surreal glow lit the cabin; it was coming from metal containers of aluminium powder used for marking the sea above enemy submarines. They had burst and scattered the contents over everything, even the bodies sprawled on the floor.

There was a movement, a groan. It was Fred Banting. He lay on the floor with his head close to a bulkhead, obviously injured, but still alive. Joe fetched a torch and examined him. There was a gaping head wound and a broken arm.

His moans became louder as the pilot struggled to bring him to a seated position, manhandling him to a folding bunk attached to the cabin side. It was then that Banting began to speak, rambling on about what Joe took to be highly technical medical matters. He went on and on, stopping only occasionally, even though his breathing was laboured. Joe clapped a dressing over the gash in his head to stop the bleeding.

Finally, Banting tried to sit up. Eyes staring, he demanded that Joe write down what he was saying. 'It's very important…'

Propping a notebook on his knee, pencil poised in the beam of the torch, he prompted Banting.

'Right, Chief. Carry on.'

With Joe pretending to take down the gasped sentences in the beam of the torch, Banting seemed to calm down. When the voice petered out, Joe saw that Fred was no longer conscious. Joe himself, exhausted, also fell asleep, waking to a grey dawn.

There was utter silence. Not even a bird called.

After having his wound dressed again and a sling made for the shattered arm, the injured man was still unconscious, and the pilot made his way outside to have a look at the damage.

Luck had been on their side to a certain extent, as while the underside of the fuselage had been torn open by the sharp rocks, the passenger area was relatively undamaged. The force of the crash had flung the occupants against bulkheads and parts of the airframe, in two cases, fatally.

Still unsteady, Joe began an attempt to make rough snowshoes from pieces of wreckage strapped to his flying boots with wire.

Walking was difficult. After half an hour of slow progress searching for a railway line or a farm, he decided to go back, worried that his passenger might have fallen out of the bunk, even although he had been tightly strapped in.

He arrived back to a scene of tragedy. Banting was face down in the snow, close by the wreck. On his hands were the gloves Collip had given him. He was dead. Unable to lift him, Joe covered the body with a parachute and clambered back inside the plane.

* * *

At Gander, no search could be mounted as, once more, the weather closed in. Unable to raise T9449 on the radio after the message asking for bearings, a 'missing plane' message was sent out to all shipping in the area.

It was not until Friday that searchers could fly out, just about the time that Fred Banting was dragging himself out of the wrecked plane and Joe was struggling on his makeshift snowshoes to find help.

The pilot both heard and saw reconnaissance planes overhead during the agonisingly long weekend, but no one sighted the wreckage in the little clearing surrounded by tall firs.

He tried lighting fires, then trudged round the plane with the aluminium powder, spelling out a message on the snow: 'THREE DEAD. JOE.'

On Monday, he was about to set off again when the crashed plane and the message were spotted. Running clear of the wreck, Joe waved his arms above his head and saw the wings of the rescue plane dip in response. As it flew over him, a cylinder floated down on a small parachute. It contained a spirit stove, food and coffee. It was very welcome, as there was no means of heating what little food was on board and the cold was penetrating, especially at night.

* * *

In Toronto, the Royal (Canadian) Air Force informed Banting's relatives and colleagues about T9449 being missing late on Friday night. Professor Duncan Graham brought the news personally to Henrietta. Fred's father went to be with her at home. He found her distraught.

'He was going to retire when he came home from England. What happened? How can I carry on without him?'

William Banting did his best.

'We don't know he's been killed. Try to be calm, Henrietta. Fred wouldn't want to see you like this…'

The *Toronto Star*'s headline next day told the story in one line:

BANTING KILLED IN AIR CRASH

Joe Mackey welcomed the rescue party with open arms. The plane crew who had spotted him had dropped a message to a group of rabbit hunters seen on the hills nearby. The Newfoundlanders trekked to the site and took the survivor back to civilisation for medical attention.

Search of the wreck produced the briefcase that Fred had with him at all times. They contained the diaries entered so meticulously by their owner every day of his adult life.

The entries told more of his character and motivation after his death than many people understood during his life.

Soldiers arrived next, putting a guard on the plane and taking the bodies to the nearest town, Musgrave Harbour, twelve miles away, where they were laid in the Orange Lodge. From there, removal of the dead had to wait, once more because of the weather, but three days later, ski-equipped planes touched down and prepared to take them to back to the mainland. Watched by most of the people of Musgrave Harbour, the coffins were brought out as the Salvation Army band played a hymn and the National Anthem.

It was a lowly tribute compared with the full military ceremony carried out in Toronto.

Banting's coffin, draped with the Canadian flag, was borne on a gun carriage along a route lined with two hundred troops.

As an Air Force band played a funeral march, the cortege moved slowly through the town centre to Mount Pleasant Cemetery.

Three rifle volleys were fired over the grave, a bugler played the 'Last Post', and his fellow officers, rigidly at attention, saluted as the coffin was lowered from sight.

Fred Banting, farmer's son from Alliston, Ontario, had come a long, long way from wearing his sister's button-sided boots on his way to school because it was too cold in winter to walk barefooted.

POSTSCRIPT

Joe Mackey sold his story for a considerable sum to the Toronto Star. *He gave the money to Snailham's three children, orphaned when their father died.*

26-year-old RAF First Officer William Bird, an Englishman from Kettering, was interred at Gander. He had one son.

Who, then, discovered Insulin?

Fred Banting, the man who started the ball rolling? Young Charley Best, caught in the hot flame of hatred that Banting levelled at the professor? Collip, who found the solution within one month, after eight spent by the others?

Finally Macleod, the reserved academic forced out of his place in Toronto? It is said that, without his guiding advice, the accolade would have gone to another country.

The Cure

The cure is here. After years of research, a process involving injections of clusters of Islets of Langerhans into the liver of several patients has been carried out in Canada and in 2005, in Britain. The liver has acted as a substitute pancreas in that it begins to produce Insulin.

Several patients have been able to discontinue their daily injections, but most have had to carry on with one or more injections daily. While there has been great success in this 'cure' for diabetes, the long-term effects of anti-rejection drugs involved in the treatment are not yet known. Until they are, the treatment will not be available worldwide.

REFERENCE BOOKS

Michael Bliss (Professor of History, Toronto University) *The Discovery of Insulin* (1982)

Michael Bliss (Professor of History, Toronto University) *Banting* (1984)

Michael Williams (Physician to the Aberdeen Royal Hospital) *Macleod. The Co-discoverer of Insulin* (1993)